W9-BHO-859

Williamsburg®

THE FINEST REPRODUCTIONS OF EIGHTEENTH-CENTURY FURNISHINGS

TABLE OF CONTENTS

COLONIAL WILLIAMSBURG
A PLACE IN HISTORY

Eighteenth-century Williamsburg, the capital of the colony of Virginia, owed its inception to politics, its design to human ingenuity, and its prosperity to government, commerce, and war. Jamestown, Virginia's (and America's) first English settlement and first capital, proved ill-suited to defense, to trade, to agriculture, to life itself. After the fourth statehouse was destroyed by fire, the colony's legislators decided to find another, better location for the seat of government. Several settlements bid to be selected. Middle Plantation, where the College of William and Mary, Bruton Parish Church, and a few taverns and farmhouses were located, won out.

The General Assembly voted to move the capital from Jamestown to Middle Plantation in 1699. Lieutenant Governor Francis Nicholson laid the town out along the mile-long axial street named for the Duke of Gloucester. Building commenced on the Capitol, Governor's Palace, public jail, powder magazine, and a new, more stately church for Bruton Parish. Another governor, Alexander Spotswood, a veteran of the Duke of Marlborough's armies, poured his energies and ideas into many of these major construction projects. The open spaces along the main street and the Palace green soon began to be filled in with houses, stores, and taverns. Less substantial buildings — tenements, stables, kitchens, dairies, smokehouses — appeared along the back streets and behind the buildings that lined the main thoroughfare. A miscellany of settlement crept out along the roads to the town's two ports, Capitol and College landings, eventually reaching the landings themselves.

The cultivation and export of tobacco fueled the colony's rapid growth during the first half of the eighteenth century. Men and women of African descent, held as slaves in bondage for life, formed the core of Virginia's labor force. As the colony prospered so did its capital city, Williamsburg. Though never larger in size than a middling English county town, Virginia's metropolis became Virginia's center of imperial rule, transatlantic trade, enlightened ideas, and genteel fashion. Williamsburg served the populace of the surrounding counties as a marketplace for goods and services, as a legal, administrative, and religious center, and as a resort for shopping, information, and diversion. But the capital, we need to remember, was also a complex urban community with its own patterns of work, family life, and cultural activities. Within Williamsburg's year-round population of some two thousand souls, half of whom were black, a rich tapestry of personal, familial, work, social, racial, gender, and cultural relationships could be found.

By the late 1930s most of the major buildings of eighteenth-century Williamsburg had been restored or reconstructed thanks to the generosity of John D. Rockefeller, Jr. Phase II involved filling in the gaps with dwellings, shops, and taverns. So that Mr. Rockefeller could envision the ultimate restoration of the town, Singleton P. Moorehead, Resident Architect of Colonial Williamsburg, rendered elevations of all streets in the Historic Area with the proposed reconstructions. Using these sketches as his guide, Mr. Rockefeller toured the town in his car to determine whether to continue the restoration of the historic site. These simple renderings convinced him to fund more buildings, and then, as Moorehead recalled in his reminiscences, "the fun really started."

A portion of Moorehead's sketch of Palace Green is shown here, including Bruton Parish Church, the George Wythe House, the Elkanah Deane House, the Robert Carter House, the Governor's Palace, and the Brush-Everard House.

In the quarter-century before the colonies broke with Great Britain, Williamsburg reached its ascendancy. It was a period marked in its early years by Great Britain's seven-year war for empire with France, and in its later years by visibly growing prosperity and increasingly bitter disagreement between the parent parliament in London and several provincial legislatures in Williamsburg and the other colonial capitals of British North America. In the Capitol at Williamsburg, patriot burgesses such as Patrick Henry protested parliamentary taxation by asserting their right as freeborn Englishmen to be taxed only by representatives of their own choosing. When British authorities removed all but a few of their taxes but bluntly reasserted their parliament's sovereign right to tax the king's subjects wherever they might reside, Thomas Jefferson, George Mason, James Madison, George Washington, and

other Virginians claimed their right to govern themselves by virtue of their humanity and the logic of common sense.

Many other Americans, of course, joined these Virginians in defending their countrymen's liberties against what they came to regard as British tyranny. They fought for and won their independence. And they then fashioned governments and institutions of self-rule, many of which guide our lives to this day. But freedom's story is, in truth, not so simple. For black Virginians, freedom seemed more likely to be found fighting beside their masters' enemies, the British, than in supporting the American cause. A number of them joined the king's forces, fought for their freedom under the flag of Great Britain, and were liberated at the end of the Revolutionary War. Most black Virginians, however, sat out the great struggle for American independence. Their children and grandchildren would live their lives as that great anomaly, that painful paradox: as slaves in a free land.

These are the events, the personalities, the ideas from our national past that can be experienced, appreciated, and learned at Colonial Williamsburg today. Virginia's old capital was saved from destruction in our century and is still in the process of being restored to its appearance during the years when colonists of English, African, and European descent fashioned from their lives together a new order, an American society and culture, and fought for, won, and then struggled to secure a new day of freedom and prosperity for all. In the Historic Area, in the museums, and at Carter's Grove plantation this is the story that is told. It is told through numerous sites and a variety of programs, exhibitions, demonstrations, reenactments, character interpretations, tours, and holiday events. There are experiences for all types, for every age, for every interest. This is where America began. This is America's Williamsburg.

— DENNIS A. O'TOOLE

Dennis A. O'Toole, *vice president and chief education officer for the Colonial Williamsburg Foundation, received a Ph.D. in history from Brown University. He is an enthusiastic advocate of museums and historic sites as classrooms and has spearheaded many innovative interpretive efforts at Colonial Williamsburg.*

William Dering combined the professions of portrait painter and dancing master when he was in Williamsburg in the 1740s. His spirited likeness of young George Booth of Belleville plantation in Gloucester County, Virginia, includes fanciful versions of baroque conventions such as the female busts and the background vista of gardens and river.

Cabinetmaker Benjamin Bucktrout of Williamsburg stamped his name into the back of this Masonic master's chair between 1767 and 1770. Its ceremonial scale and symbolic decoration were no doubt a collaboration between the Masonic lodge as patron and Bucktrout as tradesman. He had access, via Chippendale's *Gentleman and Cabinet-Maker's Director*, which has been documented in his shop, to current London rococo styles. Chippendale shows a dolphin leg on "French chairs"; the dolphin leg was the most labor intensive and therefore the most expensive sort illustrated.

The decoration on this polychromed salt-glazed stoneware inkwell, with its painting of a man writing with quill pen and ink, creates a visual pun. It was made in a Staffordshire, England, pottery about 1760.

This tall clock, made about 1700 by Thomas Tompion for William III's palace at Hampton Court, is an object too elaborate for Historic Area exhibition buildings. Nevertheless, it is an important component of Colonial Williamsburg's study collection of antiques. Its masterful baroque design, incorporating burl walnut veneers and gilded bronze mounts, its royal provenance, and the technological sophistication of its movement (which runs for three months on a single winding and contains a perpetual calendar allowing for leap year) make it the *superlative object in the collection.*

STYLE IN SEVENTEENTH- AND EIGHTEENTH-CENTURY

DECORATIVE ARTS

The Colonial Williamsburg Foundation has been collecting the decorative furnishings of the period 1650–1820 for over sixty years, building one of the world's premier assemblages of English and American antiques. We use these artifacts to interpret the past in two contexts. In the Historic Area, a living history museum, we re-create a slice of colonial Virginia in period house museums and tradesmen's shops and use the kinds of objects, both locally made and imported from England, that were there in the eighteenth century. Since 1985 the Historic Area has been complemented by a decorative arts museum, the DeWitt Wallace Gallery, where we show a study collection of English and American antiques as art objects, outside a domestic context. There we can contrast the products of Williamsburg with those of other colonial centers — Philadelphia, Boston, and Newport, for example — and with English pieces made for royal palaces, too elaborate for the province of colonial Virginia.

Architecture and interior decoration and furnishings have always been status symbols, a means of announcing one's wealth and position to the world. As such, they are subject to the vagaries of fashion, with members of each generation rebuilding or redecorating to enhance their social standing.

Of the traditional and time-honored methods of organizing the arts, that of dividing them into chronological periods according to artistic style or fashion is probably the most widely accepted. The styles represented in the Colonial Williamsburg collection comprise four large art historical periods: baroque, circa 1660–1710; late baroque, circa 1710–1745; rococo, circa 1745–1770; and neoclassical, circa 1770–1810. The characteristics of these styles appear in architecture, painting, sculpture — even in dance and music — at the same time as in furnishings. Using art historical designations rather than monarchs' or furniture designers' names allows us to cross geographic and political barriers and to relate the decorative trends in many media — furniture, ceramics, textiles, metals — throughout the western world. For example, silver made in Paris and furniture made in London in the 1750s bear many stylistic similarities; the description *rococo* applies to both, but *Georgian* or *Chippendale* or *Louis XV* do not.

Styles did not evolve in a vacuum. They were influenced by trade, politics, religion, and other factors. Civil wars, royal marriages, scientific progress, world exploration, and the industrial revolution all contributed to the evolution of styles in the arts. Nor did styles change overnight, especially in provincial areas like Scandinavia or the American colonies. We hope that the time line and the charts on the following pages will help to clarify the decorative relationships between objects of various media within each stylistic era.

ELIZABETH P. GUSLER

Elizabeth P. Gusler, *Teaching Curator, trains historical interpreters for the exhibition buildings and the DeWitt Wallace Decorative Arts Gallery. She is preparing a book on style in English and American decorative arts of the seventeenth and eighteenth centuries.*

Intimate objects are as important to the collection as grand-scale masterpieces. This porcelain drummer boy, made at the Bow factory around 1760-1765, is rococo in its palette and asymmetrical stance.

All objects illustrated are antiques in the collection of the Colonial Williamsburg Foundation. They may be seen in the exhibition buildings in the Historic Area and in the DeWitt Wallace Decorative Arts Gallery.

When this hot water urn was made about 1770, Birmingham was the center of the English metalworking industry, and factories there specialized in making enamels and ormolu (gilded bronze) mounts like those on this urn. The diaper work pattern of pink rosettes on a blue-green background, the asymmetrical handles, the pierced base, and the idyllic landscapes within gilded cartouches combine to create a masterful rococo statement.

"The best is nott too good for you" boasts this slipware cup. Dated 1697, it was made in the Staffordshire area of England. Its decoration combines the newly exotic tulip motif with the vigor of traditional English pottery.

Sir Robert Godschall, once Lord Mayor of London, commissioned Peter Archambo I to make this silver gilt salver in 1744/45. Its cast and chased border of C and S scrolls, grapes, and ruffled shells make it a masterwork of rococo design.

BAROQUE
circa 1660 to circa 1710

Renaissance classicism is the pervasive aesthethic of the western world

LOUIS XIV
1643-1715

After great unrest in France and civil war in England, Louis XIV and Charles II reestablish royal authority and use classical Italian baroque style as version author-itative of "state" style

1682 — Versailles declared seat of government in France — becomes a glorious monument of full French baroque "kingly" style

1662 — Charles II marries Catherine of Braganza, who brings Portuguese trading empire as her dowry — English Oriental trade strengthened

1685 — Louis XIV revokes Edict of Nantes, law protecting Protestants [Huguenots]; many artisans flee to Holland and England

1660 — restoration of monarchy in England; nobility rebuilds houses destroyed in civil war

1660-1680 — Peter Lely is court painter in England

PURITAN COMMONWEALTH
1649-1660

CHARLES II
1660-1685

JAMES II
1685-1688

WILLIAM III and MARY II
1689-1702

1600s — European East India companies compete for the highly lucrative Oriental trade and spawn demand for luxury consumer goods from the East

Dutch influence (incorporating Italian mannerism and the French baroque style) in English arts and architecture

1636 — Fairbanks house begun in Dedham, Massachusetts

1666 — fire destroys medieval London; Sir Christopher Wren rebuilds through end of century as baroque city — St. Paul's Cathedral is monument of this style

This time line is intended to help you understand how events affected the arts of seventeenth- and eighteenth-century England and America.

Styles do not develop in a vacuum. Historical events — world exploration and trade, politics, wars, commerce, technology, religion, ideologies — all affect the arts. Neither do styles change overnight. They evolve slowly, radiating from a style center — Paris was the leader in decorative trends in eighteenth-century Europe — to provincial areas.

Read the time line from left to right to see how styles evolved as colors change in the spectrum. Look at it from top to bottom to see how Continental trends affected English and American products.

—ELIZABETH P. GUSLER
Teaching Curator

Architecture and furnish-ings made and used in New World based upon late mannerist styles popular with Dutch and English middle classes

ca. 1674 — Elizabeth Freake and baby Mary of Boston painted by unknown artist

1676 — Bacon's Rebellion in Virginia

1693 — College of William and Mary in Williamsburg chartered

ca. 1682 — St. Luke's Church, Isle of Wight County, Virginia, built in Gothic style

1650

1675

LATE BAROQUE
circa 1710 to circa 1745

1715 — death of Louis XIV; beginning of *Régence* period and style in France

1717 — painter Watteau presents "Embarkation for the Island of Cytherea" to French Academy. This "fête galante" style influential on rococo decoration

1730s — beginning of great influence of French *ornemanistes* or designer/engravers on rococo style in all European countries

1735 — Linnaeus, *Systema Naturae* for naming and classifying plants and animals

1685-1750 — Johann S. Bach
1685-1759 — Georg F. Handel — greatest baroque composers

1680s-1723 — Godfrey Kneller is court painter in England

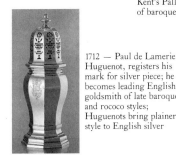

1712 — Paul de Lamerie, Huguenot, registers his mark for silver piece; he becomes leading English goldsmith of late baroque and rococo styles; Huguenots bring plainer style to English silver

1720s to 1740s: plainer style in portraits and furniture mingled with William Kent's Palladian version of baroque decoration

1727 — Lord Burlington and William Kent publish *Designs of Inigo Jones*; popularize Palladian style

1720s to 1760s: boom in building of country seats/power houses: spread of Palladianism and the influence of architectural pattern books

| ANNE 1702-1714 | GEORGE I 1714-1727 | GEORGE II 1727-1760 |

1700-1705 — Sir John Vanbrugh designs Blenheim Palace for the Duke of Marlborough

1735 — William Hogarth publishes *A Rake's Progress*

1731 — Mark Catesby publishes first volume of *Natural History of Carolina, Florida and the Bahama Islands*

1730s to 1770s — japanning of furniture popular in Boston

ca. 1740 — Drayton Hall, Palladian plantation house, built near Charleston, South Carolina

ca. 1700 — John Coney makes silver sugar box in Boston

1728 — Old State House built in Boston

1733 — Parliament removes import tax on woods, allowing mahogany to become dominant cabinet wood

1699 — capital of Virginia moved from Jamestown to Williamsburg; baroque town plan developed

1715 — Governor's Palace in Williamsburg occupied

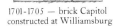

1701-1705 — brick Capitol constructed at Williamsburg

1726 — Mann Page I begins building Rosewell, grandest house in 18th-century Virginia, in Gloucester County

ROCOCO
circa 1745 to circa 1770

EUROPE

1748 — first publication of excavations at Pompeii and Herculaneum, precursors of neoclassicism

1751 — Denis Diderot begins *Encyclopédie*, an Enlightenment multi-volume work illustrating technical processes and natural phenomena

1749 — Handel's brilliant baroque *Music for the Royal Fire-works* performed in London

1763 — Voltaire publishes *Treatise on Tolerance*

1764 — Mozart gives concert at Ranelagh Gardens in London

1750s — Capability Brown begins transforming English landscape garden from geometric to natural style

1762 — Josiah Wedgwood perfects creamware; gives breakfast service to Queen Charlotte

1760s — Robert Adam designing Kedleston

1745 — porcelain (soft paste) developed at Chelsea Factory near London

1752 — copperplate printing on textiles developed in England

1762 — Matthew Boulton establishes Soho Manufactory for production of metal goods in Birmingham

GEORGE II
1727-1760

ENGLAND

1754 — Thomas Chippendale publishes *The Gentleman and Cabinet-Maker's Director*, influential rococo pattern book

1760s — Thomas Frye engraves mezzotint portraits

ca. 1770 — John Cadwalader building and furnishing his elegant Philadelphia townhouse

1770 — Paul Revere engraves "The Bloody Massacre . . . Boston" print

AMERICA

1748 — Redwood Library, Newport, Rhode Island; Peter Harrison, architect

1754-1763 — French and Indian or Seven Years' War

1765 — John Singleton Copley paints John Hancock

1769 — Thomas Jefferson begins building Monticello

VIRGINIA

1750s to 1770s — John Wollaston, John Hesselius, and John Durand paint rococo portraits of Virginia gentry, including members of the Page, Custis, Carter, and Lewis families

By 1750s plantation "great houses" — Carter's Grove, Westover, Stratford — built along tidewater rivers

ca. 1770 — Isaac Zane operates Marlboro Furnace near Winchester, Virginia

1750

NEOCLASSICAL
circa 1770 to circa 1820

1789 — French Revolution begins

1775 — James Watt enters partnership with Matthew Boulton to manufacture steam engines

1775 — Josiah Wedgwood perfects jasperware

1760s — process of fusing silver to copper core — "Sheffield plating" — widely used in manufacture of metals

1788 — George Hepplewhite publishes *Cabinetmaker & Upholsterer's Guide*

GEORGE III
1760-1820

1771 — Richard Arkwright establishes Cromford cotton spinning mill

1791 — Thomas Sheraton publishes *Cabinetmaker & Upholsterer's Drawing Book*

1776 — Adam Smith's *Wealth of Nations* discusses division of labor; prefigures industrial revolution

ca. 1770 — Thomas Affleck makes mahogany furniture for Philadelphia patrons

1760-1800 — Goddards and Townsends make block and shell case pieces in Newport, Rhode Island

1793 — Eli Whitney invents cotton gin

1780 — Charles Willson Peale paints first "state" portrait of George Washington

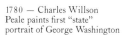

1788 — Constitution ratified

1791 — Bill of Rights

GEORGE WASHINGTON
presidency
1789-1797

1767-1770 — Benjamin Bucktrout of Williamsburg makes Masonic master's chair

1780 — capital of Virginia moves to Richmond

1798 — Thomas Jefferson designs state capitol of Virginia in temple form, beginning national architectural style for United States

1775

1800

Baroque

circa 1660 to circa 1710

This tin-glazed earthenware flower pyramid was made about 1700 at Delft, Holland, for the English market. It is typically baroque in its blending of classical elements such as columns and perspective prospects with spouts shaped like exotic sea monsters. Right: the Massachusetts walnut chest, circa 1710, shows the mannerist tendency to divide surfaces into geometric segments.

Trumpet turned legs and X-shaped stretchers are strong baroque features on this walnut dressing table made about 1725 in Philadelphia.

By the second half of the seventeenth century influences from France, Holland, and the Orient were tempering the English version of Italian mannerism into the style art historians call baroque, which flourished from about 1660 to 1710. Court styles of the first half of the century had reflected the bizarre version of Renaissance classicism popularized when Emperor Nero's "House of Gold" was uncovered in the late 1500s. Mannerist designs incorporated grotesque masks, fantastic animals, elongated figures, geometric panels, applied strapwork and bosses, and twisted columns. Elizabeth Shrewsbury's Hardwick Hall is a surviving English great house with mannerist architectural detail and furnishings.

This delft charger, made in England about 1690, probably depicts Charles II and celebrates the restoration of the British monarchy.

Western fascination with the East is obvious in the details of this crewel embroidered bed hanging. It was probably made in England by professional needleworkers between 1650 and 1700.

A bold columnar shaft and octagonal base combine handsomely in this rare pewter candlestick made in London around 1680.

The restoration of the English monarchy in 1660 marked a watershed in English architecture and furnishings, and so is the starting point for Colonial Williamsburg's collection of decorative arts. Many of Charles II's courtiers had sacrificed their ancestral homes to the royalist cause during the civil war, and were ready to rebuild in celebration of their king's return. Countering Puritan austerity of the previous two decades, they embraced the return to luxury and the Continental styles that the new king had come to favor during his exile in France and the Low Countries.

Engraved tendrils and imaginary winged creatures ("grotesques" in the vocabulary of baroque design) decorate the surface of this silver gilt cup made in London about 1685.

Plump cherubs, a hallmark of baroque design, top the boldly sculptural silvered frame of a looking glass made in England about 1670. The glass was likely part of a suite with matching dressing table and candlestands.

The bellied shape and vigorous chased decoration lend a voluptuous quality to this silver cup made between 1665 and 1680 in Salisbury, England.

The arm, foot (above), and crest rail (below) of an English walnut armchair of the 1680s demonstrate how the cabinetmaker used and varied the scroll motif as Bach varied a musical motif in composing a fugue.

Louis XIV's splendid gardens, architecture, and interiors at Versailles were making the French court the leader of European style. Englishmen copied this French version of classical baroque style in their houses and furnishings. Louis XIV unwittingly provided England with a talented labor pool of upholsterers, goldsmiths, blacksmiths, painters, and silk weavers when in 1685 he revoked the Edict of Nantes, the law that had protected Protestants (Huguenots) from persecution. Much of the artisan class of France was Huguenot, so they fled to more tolerant Holland and England, infusing Continental sophistication into the native arts of those countries. Further inspiration came via Dutch craftsmen patronized by their countryman William III, king of England from 1689 to 1702.

Continental designs were augmented by the influence of the East. Although the English had formed an East India Company in 1600, Oriental trade burgeoned after Charles II's 1662 marriage to Catherine of Braganza, the Portuguese princess who brought the port of Bombay and the vast Portuguese trading routes to England as her dowry. Chinese silks and porcelains, Japanese lacquer wares, Indian cotton chintzes, and tea and spices poured into England in quantities. Demand still exceeded supply, however, so westerners began to emulate Chinese blue and white porcelain with delft, lacquers with japanned wares, and mordant-painted chintzes with wood-blocked prints. The western fascination with the exotic, which was to last for many years as a counterpoint to classicism, began during the baroque era.

The illustrations across the bottom of these two pages depict the energetic baroque scroll in three media — walnut, earthenware, and silver. Imagining these objects in the same interior gives a feeling for the sumptuous quality of baroque decoration.

The unfaded colors and dense surface ornament of this glass beadwork basket reflect restoration period tastes without the softening effect that time takes on other media.

This superb tall clock, with movement by Thomas Tompion, was made about 1700 for King William III's residence at Hampton Court. The smooth surfaces of the burl walnut veneered case contrast with the sculptural firegilt bronze mounts. Classical allusions — the columns on the hood and the figure of Minerva — link the clock to renaissance tradition.

Visually, baroque arts are bold, sculptural, and vigorous. The tight scroll — expressed variously as a leaf, a ram's horn, a classical volute, or a more abstract form — is a favorite motif. There is a voluptuous quality to the arts of the period — think of the "Rubensesque" figures of the women who posed for Van Dyke, or of the plump cherubs on drug jars or gravestones or carved furniture. Globular shapes appear in many media, such as the "bun" feet of case pieces and the bellied bowls of delft posset pots. The spiral column, the trumpet, and urn forms are other recurrent motifs.

Luxuriant surfaces are characteristic of the baroque era. Gilding, ebonizing, caning, beadwork, raised and padded embroidery, and lavish upholstery pervaded the homes of the aristocracy. After the restraints of Puritanism the trappings of wealth were once again in fashion, so conspicuous consumption came in with a vengeance.

— ELIZABETH P. GUSLER
Teaching Curator

A boldly shaped apron, columnar legs, and ball feet help date this Virginia-made walnut tea table to about 1710.

Dated 1676 and decorated with the arms of the London Company of Carpenters, this Lambeth delft posset pot may commemorate the date when its owner was elected to a high post within the company. In comparison to the controlled formality of the silver chandelier arm at right, the scroll handles of the pot are naive, though equally bold.

Huguenot silversmith Daniel Garnier summoned his training in French classicism and formal restraint when he produced this silver chandelier for St. James Palace in the 1690s. His controlled combination of broken scrolls and gadrooning created an extremely successful object.

Late Baroque

circa 1710 to circa 1745

The naturalistic scallop shell was a popular motif of the late baroque style. It is repeated on the crest rail, seat rail, and knees of this Philadelphia walnut chair of about 1740.

The "compass seat" undulates to match the curvilinear back.

Trifid feet offered an alternative to pad or ball and claw feet during the late baroque period.

The serpentine line — Hogarth's "line of beauty" — provides the dominant aesthetic in late baroque chairs. Based upon Chinese prototypes and called "Indian chairs" in the period, elements included cabriole legs, curvilinear arms and stiles, and a solid vase-shaped splat. The negative space between splat and stile, which frequently suggested a bird's profile, was an important design component.

As baroque styles evolved in the eighteenth century, many characteristics of the earlier period were retained. Oriental themes remained popular; in fact, western craftsmen made almost direct copies of Chinese chairs and tables and tea wares that we now often accept as western forms, not as *chinoiserie*. Luxurious surfaces stayed in vogue, but in a flatter interpretation than had been popular previously: burl walnut veneers, along with solid walnut and, occasionally, mahogany, replaced the earlier oak or ebonized beech. Plain surfaces were also an option, especially in silver. Elongated forms — tall looking glasses and high-backed chairs — carried on the mannerist tendency toward attenuation.

Rich blue color and an understated ogee shape make this salt-glazed bowl successful. It was made about 1750 in a pottery in Staffordshire, England, probably by Josiah Wedgwood or William Littler.

George Wickes used the Palladian style popularized by William Kent when he made this silver soup tureen in 1737/38. Its opulence expresses a growing satisfaction that the second quarter of the eighteenth century was an "Augustan Age" in England. Wickes imaginatively incoporated the owner's crest, a griffin passant, into the design as handles.

Design concepts often appear in more than one medium: the marbleized clays of agateware parallel the use of burl walnut veneers in the late baroque period, and the hexagonal shaping on this coffeepot echoes silver versions. The eighteenth century was a golden age for English pottery, when potters such as Josiah Wedgwood were innovating techniques for shaping, glazing, and decorating wares for a growing consumer market.

The tight dynamic scroll of the early baroque loosened into a languid S-curve. It appeared in the broken scroll pediments of doorways and case pieces, in the blocking of desk interiors, and — perhaps most pervasively — in the design of chairs. The curved line that William Hogarth called the "line of beauty" was employed in the hoop backs, compass seats, and cabriole legs of the chairs of the period. This subtle harmony of curves lent a restrained elegance missing from the robust designs of the earlier baroque. The serpentine line was not new — it had been classic in eastern and western cultures for centuries. In the Orient it appeared as the vase shape, while in ancient Rome it was used in the sarcophagus. Both cultures blended in the English late baroque style, as William Kent looked to Augustan Rome for furnishings for the Palladian interiors he designed for the empire builders and Giles Grendey "japanned" the Chinese style chairs he built for his patrons.

A walnut stool made in London about 1730 sports a human mask on its skirt, ball and claw feet, and shells with pendant bellflowers on the knees, all characteristic of the late baroque style. Needlework was a popular upholstery material in the period.

The graceful serpentine leg of this Norfolk, Virginia, mahogany card table, circa 1750, ends in a pad foot.

An undulating appliquéd framework accents this window curtain. Its Indian mordant [dye fixative] painted chintz center is surrounded by a border of red and blue French woodblock-printed cottons. Made between 1750 and 1800, it subtly blends eastern and western decorative traditions.

Another variant of the S-curve was the pear shape, popular in teapots of the period. In furniture this shape was translated into bombé, or swelled bottom, case pieces made in Boston later in the century.

There were strong overtones of architecture in many designs of the late baroque period. The fronts of furniture pieces such as pedimented bookcases or clothespresses echoed the facades of buildings. The raised panels used in architectural paneling appeared in cabinetmakers' work. Hexagonal and octagonal shapes were fashionable, not only on institutional buildings like the Powder Magazine at Williamsburg, but also in domestic objects such as coffeepots. Architectural balusters, columns, and pilasters accented furniture and provided the basic shape for accessory objects such as candlesticks. Interlaced strapwork was a popular architectural ornament and was also used on silver, textiles, and furniture, particularly on chair splats. Animal motifs were used frequently by artisans of the late baroque era as an alternative to geometric, architectural ornament. Tables and chairs sported hoof feet, smooth and hairy paw feet, and ball and claw feet (derived from the oriental theme of the dragon clutching a pearl) in addition to the Chinese inspired pad foot. Lion's masks and classical human masks decorated the skirts of tables, seating furniture, and ceremonial silver vessels. Dolphin's heads supported silver salvers.

"Japanned" surfaces, imitating Oriental lacquer, were especially popular during the second quarter of the eighteenth century. Chinese motifs such as willow trees, pavilions, and fretwork are interspersed with scrolls, scallop shells, and bellflowers on this chair which was produced in the London shop of Giles Grendey about 1725.

Like many European objects made in the first flush of fascination with the East, this mahogany tea table is an almost direct copy of Chinese examples. Made circa 1735 in Williamsburg, it exhibits a restrained elegance in its understatement.

Gadrooned borders and reserves of interlaced strapwork — gilded for special effect — accent this London walnut side chair made about 1725.

The Oriental trade brought to Europe and the colonies wares designed and made for the western market. This Chinese porcelain punch bowl was made for export about 1730.

Giles Grendey's London shop made this mahogany clothespress about 1740. Its raised and shaped panels are typical of the period and are reminiscent of the shaped rim on the salver below left.

Styles of the late baroque period represent a fascination with the exotic, fueled by an "enlightened" age's exploration of the world, grounded in the secure roots of classical antiquity. The synthesis of eastern and western traditions created such objects as japanned clothespresses with chinoiserie ornament superimposed on a symmetrical architectural-type case.

— ELIZABETH P. GUSLER
Teaching Curator

The cast rim with gadrooning and cherub's masks, along with the engraved inner border of strapwork, shells, and diaperwork, define this silver gilt salver as a product of the late baroque period. Made by Thomas Farren of London about 1730, it was probably part of a royal toilet service.

Rococo

circa 1745 to circa 1770

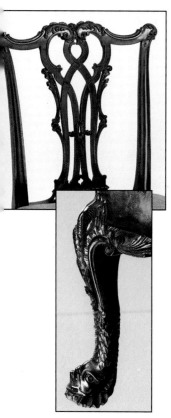

The pierced splat of the Philadelphia chair, above, has a Gothic air. This dolphin leg, above, was used on a Masonic master's chair made by Benjamin Bucktrout of Williamsburg in the late 1760s. Copied from a design in Chippendale's *Director,* it is the only known American use of this expensive leg design.

Charles Willson Peale painted Benjamin Harrison of Brandon plantation on the James River in 1775. Harrison's dignified demeanor and rich but subdued blue velvet suit exemplify the restrained elegance favored by Virginia patrons.

Huguenot silk weavers in the Spitalfields area of London wove the flower brocaded silk of this gown about 1745. Botanical motifs were popular during the rococo period, and the cabbage leaf porcelain soup tureen is similar in spirit. Made at the Bow factory near London about 1755, its interior features a painting of Roman ruins that would appear mistily through a clear broth!

By the 1740s some Englishmen, especially those who had been on the Grand Tour of the Continent, were bored with the constraints of baroque classicism and ready for decorative diversions. They turned to France, Europe's design center since the end of the seventeenth century; there they found a "modern" style of fanciful asymmetrical designs based on natural forms, especially the rock work built into grottoes in aristocratic pleasure gardens. The French word for rock work is *rocaille,* from which art historians have coined the term "rococo" to describe this stylistic period.

For years Americans have called furniture made in this style "Chippendale." Thomas Chippendale was a cabinetmaker who in 1754 published an influential pattern book, *The Gentleman and Cabinet-Maker's Director,* illustrating many rococo furniture designs. He was by no means the first or the only shop master working in this style, nor was he the only one to publish a design book. Ironically, most of the documented pieces [those for which accounts survive] from Chippendale's shop are in the neoclassic style that succeeded the rococo. Chippendale's name, therefore, is a confusing adjective for furniture, and it is further limiting as a stylistic designation because it cannot apply to metalwork, ceramics, or textiles.

Festive ribbons and flowers decorate this French brocaded silk taffeta, circa 1750-1760.

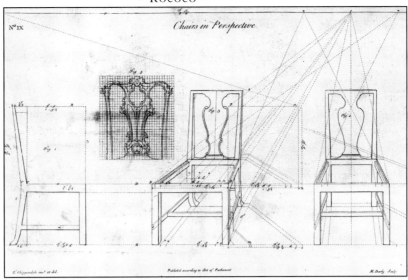

Thomas Chippendale's illustration of "Chairs in Perspective" shows various levels of decoration available to a patron, from the highly carved example shown in the grid to the "neat and plain" type requested by many southern colonists.

The rococo style is distinguished by lightness of form, whimsy, and a profusion of carved or pierced ornament. There is frequent use of asymmetry, of ribbons, and of naturalistic motifs. Chippendale described his designs in the *Director* as being in the "Gothic, Chinese, and Modern [or French]" taste. Parallel with these exotic fashions was the traditional English preference for the classic — pieces still based on ancient rules of balance and proportion. This English distaste for French excesses was particularly strong in the southern colonies of America, where patrons often stated their preference for the "neat and plain" version of the rococo style.

Philadelphia cabinetmaker Thomas Affleck made this chest on chest about 1775 for David Deshler, a Germantown merchant. The cast ornamental brasses, the swirling grain of the mahogany drawer fronts, the piercing of the pediment, and the delicate carving of the rosettes and finial contribute a rococo lightness to an otherwise massive piece.

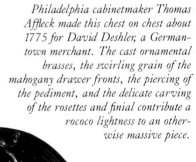

With its swirling, asymmetrical shape and rich blue and gold decoration, this porcelain candlestick is particularly French in feeling.

Made at the Chelsea factory near London about 1765, the figures and foliage that decorate this candlestick convey that quality of pastoral fantasy that was an important component of the rococo style.

This English upholstery cotton of about 1770 was printed with a copperplate engraved with chinoiserie scenes. The exotic birds in the upper left appear frequently on English pottery and porcelain of the period.

This walnut chest of drawers made in Virginia about 1770 exhibits the neat and plain variation of the Chinese taste that was popular with southern patrons.

Fluid fronds of gilded wood — these wall brackets were intended to look as delicate as the porcelain ornaments displayed upon them. The "56 pieces of ornamental china" that Lord Botetourt had at the Governor's Palace in the late 1760s might have been shown off on such brackets in his English houses.

Mahogany was the favored cabinet wood of the period. Its dense grain allowed delicate acanthus and floral carving and gave it the strength for the piercing characteristic of rococo designs. The Chinese inspired straight Marlborough leg was a popular option on chairs and tables. While the cabriole leg continued in use, the most fashionable type of foot was the scroll, except in the colonies where the ball and claw foot remained popular.

Mahogany fretwork was echoed in pierced brasses on furniture and firearms, and in many other pierced metal objects such as silver bread baskets or japanned tin trays. English porcelain, developed in the 1740s, was a perfect vehicle for the rococo style. Pierced porcelain baskets and whimsical figures, called "ornamental china" in period inventories, were all the rage.

Pagoda and pine-apple decorate a plate of the cast-iron stove made in 1770 by Abraham Buzaglo of London for presentation by Lord Botetourt to the Virginia House of Burgesses.

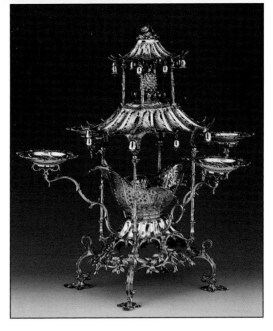

A pagoda-inspired silver epergne, or dessert centerpiece, was the height of elegance for a fashionable hostess. Thomas Pitts of London made this example in 1762/63. Its top section is remarkably similar to the ornament on the cast-iron stove plate at left.

A red dragon and prunus blossoms — typical decoration on Japanese Kakiemon wares — enhance this fluted porcelain bowl made at Chelsea between 1750 and 1753.

These figures of Harlequin and Columbine from the Italian commedia dell'arte *capture the whimsical spirit of the rococo. The Bow factory near London made them in soft-paste porcelain about 1760.*

Silk brocades of the period, ornamented with flowers that seem to have been randomly strewn about, have an open quality as well. Copperplate printing on textiles, a development of the early 1750s, allowed monochromatic pastoral or Oriental scenes or floral designs to be quickly printed on upholstery fabric, thus providing an English-made alternative to the too popular imported Indian chintzes.

The rococo was a complex style, wearing many faces. Flamboyant French pieces, with their elaborate carving and excessive asymmetry, appear at generally the upper end of the spectrum. More restrained or modest tastes preferred the aesthetic of the "neat and plain" that anchors the other end of a patron's wide range of possible choices within this style.

— ELIZABETH P. GUSLER
Teaching Curator

Marlborough legs, pagoda crest rail and arm motifs, fretwork, and caning are all chinoiserie aspects of this settee. Mahogany's dense grain allows such a delicate piece of furniture to serve for seating. It was part of a large suite of seating furniture made in London about 1760.

Embroidered swags and tassels decorate this southern whitework cotton counterpane. Made between 1780 and 1820, it is typical of the sort of handmade bed covering that many young women made for their marriage beds.

Neoclassical

circa 1770 to circa 1820

Books on the excavations at Pompeii and Herculaneum in southern Italy in the late 1740s sparked a renewed wave of interest in ancient civilization. The new classicism was not confined to the monumental public architecture — such as temples — that had inspired the previous eras. Instead, it was a domestic version of Roman decoration, derived from the interiors of Pompeiian houses, that was brought to light and now gained prominence.

The main proponent of neoclassicism in England was Scottish architect Robert Adam, who had studied the ruins in Italy. The English aristocracy commissioned him to build (or redesign) and decorate houses in the new taste; Osterley, Harewood, and Kedleston are surviving examples of his work. Adam frequently subcontracted Thomas Chippendale and Josiah Wedgwood to provide furnishings for his decorative schemes.

Josiah Wedgwood's jasperware, an unglazed stoneware, reflected the palette and decoration of excavated Pompeiian interiors. His pottery made this flower container about 1780.

Matthew Boulton, called by Wedgwood the "first manufacturer in England," produced this ornamental clock at his Soho Manufactory in Birmingham. Made about 1775, its Roman figure, urn, and swag sculpture express English admiration for ancient culture.

This wine fountain centerpiece in the form of a Roman temple was made circa 1810-1820 of fused silver on copper, called Sheffield plate. Sheffield and Birmingham were the centers of the English metalworking industry.

Robert Adam designed this handsome trophy for the 1776 Richmond Cup horse races in Yorkshire, England. Adam incorporated many of the decorative details that he used in houses. Daniel Smith and Robert Sharp of London executed his design in silver gilt.

The non-architectural combination of classical details — ram's heads, swags, Greek key and wave motifs, and paterae — is typical of neoclassic useful wares. Industrial innovations such as steel dies that could stamp out components encouraged this sort of aggregate design. This silver candlestick is one of six made at Sheffield in 1774/75 and marked with the crest of the Custis family of Virginia that descended in the Custis/Washington and Lee families.

Adam introduced the neoclassic style to England in the 1760s, but it did not really gain wide favor in America until after the Revolution. Then the political and philosophical ideals of the new United States echoed those of the Roman Republic, so the style was especially popular and appropriate. Its most enthusiastic American advocate was Thomas Jefferson, who designed his own home, Monticello, as well as the capitol of Virginia and the University of Virginia in the neoclassical style.

Because neoclassical designs were based upon small-scale architecture and interior decoration, they were lighter in feeling than preceding styles of classical inspiration. Vertical stripes — on upholstery, wallpaper, and on clothing — enhance this feeling of lightness. Elements such as the tapered legs of chairs and tables appear slightly attenuated. Two English cabinetmakers, George Hepplewhite and Thomas Sheraton, published design books and so made their own names synonymous with furniture in the neoclassical style.

When this mahogany sideboard was made in New York about 1800, it was a new furniture form. Hepplewhite suggested that the utility of its combined storage and serving functions rendered a dining room "incomplete without a sideboard."

Josiah Wedgwood's factory made this serving dish about 1775 using two fashionable innovations — his cream colored earthenware, called "Queen's ware," and transfer-printed decoration.

Virginian Lucy Burwell enjoyed fashionable London silver at her Carter Hall plantation near Winchester. This hot water urn, part of a tea service decorated with her "bright cut" monogram, bears hallmarks for 1797/98.

Oval brasses stamped with Roman temples accent this serpentine walnut chest of drawers made near Winchester, Virginia, about 1810.

Delicate swags and ovals decorate this 1790s English fan with a Suffolk, Virginia, history.

The urn, the ram's head, the Greek key, the Greek wave, and the anthemion were frequently used to decorate neoclassical objects. The oval was a popular shape, used for the tops of Pembroke tables, for looking glass frames, for chair backs, and for furniture brasses. Inlay replaced carving as the decorative surface of furniture. Inlaid ovals, swags, bellflowers, and eagles were common motifs.

Bright-cut engraving achieved on silver an effect similar to inlay on wood. The shallow decoration could also be used on Sheffield plate, the cheaper alternative to sterling silver that was mass marketed in the late eighteenth century.

Inlaid details on this tall clock from Harrisonburg, Virginia, circa 1815, include eagles, fan, urns, and simulated dentil molding.

Shield backed chairs were shown in the pattern books of both Hepplewhite and Sheraton. This mahogany example was made in New York City about 1795.

English manufacturers did not scruple to supply the American market with goods celebrating victory in the war with the mother country. The copperplate-printed valance at right, faded from purple to sepia, was made about 1785 and was used by the Galt family of Williamsburg. The Galts' bedstead, displayed in the George Wythe house, is hung with reproductions of the original bed hangings.

English potter Ralph Wood, Sr., made this earthenware figure of the Roman goddess Diana about 1770 to decorate a mantel or dining table.

Wedgwood's cream colored earthenware, called "Queen's Ware" in honor of Queen Charlotte's patronage, was the popular tableware of the time. It was often left undecorated as a reflection of the pure philosophical and moral ideals of the time. His ornamental jasperware, an unglazed stoneware best known in blue and white, frequently featured classical scenes or figures; it has become an icon of the period.

By the 1820s the decorative influence of Napoleon's Egyptian campaigns was realized in American decorative arts. The stylistic results were massive forms akin to baroque designs. In furnishings as in all things, fashion is cyclical: the more things change, the more they stay the same.

— ELIZABETH P. GUSLER
Teaching Curator

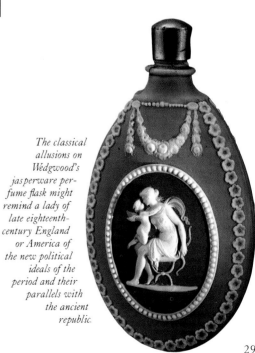

The classical allusions on Wedgwood's jasperware perfume flask might remind a lady of late eighteenth-century England or America of the new political ideals of the period and their parallels with the ancient republic.

29

Portrait prints provided loyal subjects with pictures of their monarch.

Occasionally important objects can be documented in the Historic Area when the originals have not survived. The "warming machines" that Lord Botetourt ordered for the Palace are good examples. This reproduction was carefully researched and adapted from the original stove that Botetourt gave to the colony for use in the Capitol; it survived the move to Richmond and is now on loan to Colonial Williamsburg.

Prints offered a means of reproducing paintings for a broader audience. Prints of the "Gods in Love," copied from paintings by Titian, are now in a dressing closet in the Governor's Palace.

THE HISTORICAL USE OF
REPRODUCTIONS

Reproductions of works of art have a long and honorable history. They have been sought by acquisitive people for many hundreds of years as copies or representations of someone or something divine, admirable, or especially felicitous. For well over a thousand years, for example, pilgrims to great religious centers have bought icons. From the Renaissance onward travelers to Italy have acquired paintings, drawings, prints, sculpture — all copies of famous originals. For the last hundred years untold millions of people have purchased all kinds of color prints of great monuments they have actually seen (or maybe hoped someday to see) in a distant place. They have done so because they wanted a souvenir of something worthy, a tangible object they believed would recall to their daily lives their memorable experience of the original. They bought something, in other words, that would add some dignity, pleasure, or other meaning to their existence.

Although leading collectors today often disavow reproductions, it was not always so. One of the most discriminating and creative men ever associated with Williamsburg was Thomas Jefferson. In addition to his college education here, he received some of the most formative cultural lessons of his life from gentlemen of the town who befriended him. His early plan for a collection at Monticello featured almost exclusively copies of classical statues. Jefferson clearly believed it appropriate and cultured to learn from and be improved by association with renowned prototypes. Later he expanded his collection to include paintings and prints of famous religious, political, and cultural figures and events copied from well-known originals. Like many educated people of his time, he believed that reproductions served an invaluable purpose, that they were ennobling and dignifying because they recalled a great original with proven powers to arouse profound emotional and intellectual responses.

The Colonial Williamsburg Reproductions Program was set up for somewhat the same purpose over fifty years ago by John D. Rockefeller, Jr. Having formed several great collections of original works of art, Mr. Rockefeller — like many of his more thoughtful collecting contemporaries — wanted the benefits of works of art to be as widely spread as possible, as accessible and appreciated as they could be made. In this case, rather than copies of some of the greatest religious or secular items, what the program would offer were reproductions of objects that people living in eighteenth-century Williamsburg might have used on a daily basis. This was perhaps a more democratic association with the art and good design of the past! A number of the originals were, of course, owned or used by some of the famous persons who played a key role in the formation of our country. But not all. There was meant to be at least as much association by the average modern citizen with the possessions of those ordinary people who had contributed so importantly to the successful struggle for self-government and their own freedom.

The word "reproduction" is understood many ways in the popular mind, but in association with Williamsburg for half a century it has been widely regarded as describing a copy that is as close to the original as modern industrial methods can possibly bring it. Curators use these reproductions in numerous rooms in the Historic Area where sufficient numbers of antiques are unobtainable or where antiques (with their inherent fragility) might be too vulnerable. These reproductions make our remarkable collections of original objects more accessible, more visible, ultimately, we hope, more understandable. They have a long and honorable history.

— GRAHAM S. HOOD

Graham S. Hood is Vice President and the Carlisle H. Humelsine Curator. Author of books on silver, paintings, and American porcelain, he has a forthcoming book on the influence of the Governor's Palace at Williamsburg on the material culture of eighteenth-century Virginia.

It was February of 1930 during a meeting at the Rockefeller home in New York when the problem first surfaced. As John D. Rockefeller, Jr. listened to the experts' plan to refurbish the Raleigh Tavern as a working inn, he grew uneasy. The building's furniture and fabrics were to be appropriate antiques and reproductions, they told him, but the tableware would have to be modern commercial patterns because suitable reproductions did not exist. Not content with partial authenticity, Mr. Rockefeller commissioned Josiah Wedgwood & Sons to reproduce chinaware from fragments of Queen's ware excavated on the tavern site. As no such china was then available in the marketplace, he suggested that "the purpose of education might be furthered by the sale of this ware" to the public. The Reproductions Program was launched.

Public response was astonishing. Visitors and collectors begged to have favorite antiques reproduced. Architects and interior designers pleaded for the opportunity to use the colors, designs, and materials they saw in the restored buildings. Department stores across the United States clamored for the distinction of being selected to sell the products from Williamsburg. The boldness and excitement of the Williamsburg experiment had caught the country's imagination in a profound way.

The demands of the Second World War slowed the Reproductions Program but within a few years after the fighting ended, a nationwide boom in babies and housing created an unprecedented demand for household goods that the Program scrambled to meet. The product line expanded to 350 items and the mail order business was revived, spreading Williamsburg's spirit of gracious living beyond the confines of the restored town.

The longevity and sheer size of the Colonial Williamsburg Reproductions Program have earned it the nickname "the granddaddy." The largest museum program in the world, it is also the only one truly national in scope, with designated *Williamsburg* Shops dotting the United States and showrooms for the trade in Atlanta and High Point. Committed to quality and education, Colonial Williamsburg's program is guided by a Review Committee of curators and historians with final say on each product. Over the years, its furniture and accessories have found their way into the White House and United States embassies overseas. In Williamsburg, reproductions are displayed in exhibition buildings and used in working kitchens, craft shops, operating taverns, guest houses, and hotels, where the rigors of daily handling prohibit the use of antiques.

A manufacturer licensed by Colonial Williamsburg is a rare commodity in today's hurry-up business world. To become affiliated with the Reproductions Program, a company must have the ability to copy an antique exactly, even if it involves the use of handwork or reproduction techniques abandoned years ago for faster, cheaper methods. Nor is Williamsburg's product line a here-today-discontinued-tomorrow group — items are carefully chosen for their enduring appeal.

Strong and steady interest in things colonial has produced the single most resilient style in American home furnishings. While the original eras of late baroque, rococo, and neoclassical maintained their popularity in America for a brief three or four decades apiece, these colonial styles as a group returned with the Centennial excitement of 1876 to assert a formidable influence on American culture and taste. In the forefront of this colonial resurgence since the 1930s, still setting the standards for quality and authenticity, stands the *Williamsburg* Reproductions Program, the granddaddy of them all.

WILLIAMSBURG Reproductions Program. This hallmark, designed from an early shipper's mark, is used to identify authentic reproductions and adaptations of seventeenth- and eighteenth-century English and American antiques in the Colonial Williamsburg Foundation collection. The products are produced by licensed manufacturers of the Foundation.

Folk Art Program. The rooster symbol, based on a nineteenth-century weather vane, identifies all products reproduced, adapted, or interpreted from objects in the Abby Aldrich Rockefeller Folk Art Center. Created by artisans and manufacturers licensed by the Foundation, the products in this program feature folk art and American country furnishings.

All products produced by licensees of the Colonial Williamsburg Foundation carry this mark. It indicates that the product meets the high standards of the Foundation and has been approved by the Products Review Committee.

This mark appears on reproductions, adaptations, and interpretations based on the buildings and furnishings of Carter's Grove plantation. One of the grand tidewater plantations of Virginia, Carter's Grove is located eight miles from Williamsburg's Historic Area and is operated and interpreted today as an integral part of the educational programs of Colonial Williamsburg.

DECORATING

FOR TWENTIETH-CENTURY INTERIORS

The eighteenth century has been called the Age of Consumerism for good reason—never in history had there been so much demand for consumer goods and, thanks to the Industrial Revolution, so much affordable merchandise to satisfy the demand. Elaborate tea sets, matched chairs by the dozen, and other items unheard of only a few decades earlier had become indispensable to genteel life by the second half of that century.

The glory of the era was its superb design. From furniture to fabrics, prints to wallpapers, the design masters of the eighteenth century reached levels of quality and aesthetic achievement the world has yet to surpass. The styles are timeless. The elegance of their lines and forms transcends their original era, allowing effortless interaction with virtually any other period.

Many Americans today choose to recapture the spirit of gentility and gracious living that Colonial Williamsburg evokes by decorating their own homes in the traditional manner. They find that the wide array of *Williamsburg* Reproductions can furnish a room's every detail or complement their own antiques and heirlooms. Those with a more eclectic outlook discover that *Williamsburg* Reproductions mix as comfortably in contemporary rooms as they do with any of today's popular decorating styles. They adapt easily to either formal or casual living, smoothing the harsh edges of our hectic world with their quiet sophistication.

Whether your castle is a rustic mountain retreat, a pleasant home in the suburbs, or an urban condominium, *Williamsburg* Reproductions are your entree into the warmer, softer life-styles of centuries past.

These rooms were decorated especially for this book and are not on display.

<table>
<tr>
<td></td>
<td></td>
<td></td>
<td></td>
<td></td>
</tr>
</table>

These rooms were decorated especially for this book and are not on display.

Williamsburg

FURNISHINGS:

TRADITIONAL IDEAS FOR MODERN TIMES

For some, *Williamsburg* furnishings represent the desire to re-create an authentic period room. For others, they represent modern warmth and amenities underscored by accents that take advantage of the craftsmanship and aesthetic of an earlier period.

There is one fundamental aspect in every interpretation of *Williamsburg* furnishings: flexibility. This attribute makes it possible to effectively and attractively combine contemporary sophistication with traditional elegance. Choose simplicity or opulence, the primitive or the highly decorative. Select pieces emphasizing urban sophistication or country informality. Opt for minimalism or a room filled with valued treasures. Create the unexpected, the delightful, the daring, but always the eminently livable.

To fire your imagination about *Williamsburg* furnishings, we have created a special group of custom designed rooms. They show how you can use the designs, colors, and textures of the eighteenth century to create your own interpretation of tradition.

Equally important, every item in this book represents detailed curatorial research combined with a rare level of craftsmanship. Items are described in terms of their construction, dimensions, and origin.

The result is a book that is easy to use and offers a wealth of possibilities for creating the look you want. *Williamsburg* furnishings: traditional ideas for contemporary times.

"Never be afraid to use color... spaces that are more traditional in feeling don't have to be dark."

THE HALLWAY OF THE GRISSELL HAY HOUSE, WILLIAMSBURG

Imagine strolling down Nicholson Street on a sunny afternoon in Williamsburg. You pass the Grissell Hay House, a classic eighteenth-century home dressed in narrow clapboards and crowned by two center-end chimneys. The front door is framed by a gracious portico, inviting you inside to explore. You turn the doorknob. The door swings open. Inside, you find a room that defines tradition in a whole new way.

"Never be afraid to use color," advises designer Gary Crain of New York City. "Spaces that are more traditional in feeling don't have to be dark. Many of these colors are true to history but used in unexpected ways."

Gary juxtaposes the quietly elegant lines of late baroque and rococo style furniture with the dazzle of their fabric coverings. The shine of marble, glass, and gold leaf balances the soft sheen of wood. A boldly patterned yet restfully colored reproduction wallpaper lightens the painted wood trim.

The result is a space that is more than a mere passageway from one room to another, but a room of its own. "Elegance. Restfulness. An inviting, uncluttered feeling. That's what we've created here."

These rooms were decorated especially for this book and are not on display.

*"We used lots of color
to create a room that people
can look at and say,
'I could live there.'"*

THE LIVING ROOM OF THE GRISSELL HAY HOUSE, WILLIAMSBURG

In the eighteenth century, when today's living room was known as the parlor, a family's most elegant furnishings were displayed to create an impression of comfort and affluence. These two attributes receive a decidedly modern twist from New York interior designer Gary Crain.

"Every piece of furniture here is a reproduction, but the room doesn't look like a museum. That's because we used lots of color to create a room that people can look at and say, 'I could live there.'"

A sunny yellow warms the room on even the rainiest days, further energizing the red striped curtains. A formal damask contrasts with the genteel elegance of the Oriental rug. A chair covering in a yellow stripe unexpectedly echoes the curtains. "But," explains Gary, "it's that pink chair that gives the room real dazzle."

These rooms were decorated especially for this book and are not on display.

*"Contrasting colors
keep this room
from being too quiet,
yet they're coordinated
— right down to the
flowers in the garden."*

THE DINING ROOM OF THE GRISSELL HAY HOUSE, WILLIAMSBURG

By now you've realized that while *Williamsburg* furnishings may be traditional, they hardly are predictable. Instead, they offer a look based directly on how you wish to interpret the traditional to fit your life-style today.

The ambience of this dining room is a perfect example. "Contrasting colors keep this room from being too quiet. Yet they're coordinated — right down to the flowers in the garden," observes Gary Crain.

The light-handed swag and jabot drapery treatment blurs the distinction between inside and outside, making the garden an integral part of the room. Blue wood trim, echoed by the plates on the mantel, cools the room. Contrasting red upholstery on the chairs gives it life. Warmly muted walls, classic lines, and restrained patterns keep it all in perfect balance.

The result is a room that encourages you to invite a few close friends over for dinner and an evening of lively conversation — a pastime as popular in the eighteenth century as it is today.

"Reproductions... mixed in with treasured antiques as well as modern accessories... give the room a look that is very personal and very livable."

THE TAVERN KITCHEN OF THE GRISSELL HAY HOUSE, WILLIAMSBURG

Taverns provided a welcome respite from the rigors of travel during the eighteenth century. They were cheery places offering hearty food, good companionship, and news about events of the day.

Step into this kitchen and you find yourself in a room offering these same attributes to busy families caught up in the fast-paced activity of the twentieth century. It is an environment that encourages conversation about work, school, community, and world events to fill the air along with the aroma of good food and the delicate clatter of silver on porcelain.

"Most of the things you see in this kitchen are reproductions, but they're mixed in with treasured antiques as well as modern accessories," explains interior designer Jackie Smith of Colonial Williamsburg's Craft House. "This gives the room a look that is very personal and very livable."

These rooms were decorated especially for this book and are not on display.

These rooms were decorated especially for this book and are not on display.

THE LIBRARY OF THE ELKANAH DEANE HOUSE, WILLIAMSBURG

Say the word "library" and it is likely to conjure up an image of heavy fringed draperies, time-darkened paneling, and dimly lighted corners. In contrast, this room offers all the coziness of the traditional library you might expect to find in an eighteenth-century structure, but with a lighter feeling for modern living.

"Shapes and patterns are the story here," explains Gary Crain. "The green and white toile draperies and wallpaper are lush but light, and they coordinate beautifully with the painted green wood. The scale and lines of the furniture are strong. Colorful stripes contrast with textured needlepoint and the reflective quality of damask." Just the spot for relaxing, catching up on correspondence, or a long, quiet read.

"Shapes and patterns are the story . . ." in this unexpectedly light yet cozy library.

*"I wanted to create a room
that was as close to a period
room as practical and show how
comfortable it could be today."*

THE MASTER BEDROOM OF THE CHISWELL-
BUCKTROUT HOUSE, WILLIAMSBURG

Of all the rooms you are seeing showing *Williamsburg*
furnishings, this is the most traditional. Explains interior
designer Jackie Smith, "I wanted to create a room that was
as close to a period room as practical and show how comfortable it could be today. So I took my inspiration for this
room directly from Thomas Chippendale's pattern book,
The Gentleman and Cabinet-Maker's Director."

In this elegant master bedroom, antiques blend
seamlessly with carefully chosen reproductions. Only a few
items, such as the lamp adapted from a delft tobacco jar,
hint at the more modern comforts we've grown accustomed
to in the twentieth century.

"When I stepped back and looked around I realized, 'This little girl has grown up!'"

THE GIRL'S BEDROOM IN THE NELSON-GALT HOUSE, WILLIAMSBURG

Anne Gray, a Colonial Williamsburg interior designer at Craft House, drew clear inspiration from this eighteenth-century home once owned by Thomas Nelson, signer of the Declaration of Independence. Yet this room is very comfortable and livable for today. "I used color to create a modern feeling. If I'd used gold instead of pink it would have been a different room."

Anne called on reproductions for traditional interest, then found new ways to use them. For example, mint julep cups double as holders for makeup brushes on the dressing table and for pencils on the chest used as a desk. These refined accessories set the room's tone. "When I stepped back and looked around I realized, 'This little girl has grown up!'"

"A little boy's room doesn't have to look like it was designed on another planet."

THE BOY'S BEDROOM IN THE GRISSELL HAY HOUSE, WILLIAMSBURG

"Little boys need a place that will accommodate pet frogs, and stacks of baseball cards. But that doesn't mean their room has to look like it was designed on another planet."

Jackie Smith has selected durable, practical reproduction fabrics, furniture, and folk art toys to create a room with a traditional feeling. Yet, it still accommodates the myriad interests of a young boy, contained in a reproduction storage chest at the foot of the bed.

These rooms were decorated especially for this book and are not on display.

These rooms were decorated especially for this book and are not on display.

"Here is a perfect example of how you can combine reproduction furniture, fabrics, and accessories with things you already have..."

WEEKEND HOME IN EAST HAMPTON, LONG ISLAND

"Here is a perfect example of how you can combine reproduction furniture, fabrics, and accessories with things you already have to create a light, airy room without that eighteenth-century seriousness," explains Gary Crain.

"You can update a beautiful club chair with *Williamsburg* chintzes. Or add dash to a camelback sofa with *Williamsburg* print throw pillows. You can combine reproduction candlesticks or china with your own books and antiques. It all works so well together."

The living room opens directly into the dining area where Gary has given an entirely new look to an old table. "We interlined the fabric for a comfortable but lush look. Sometimes, we put a mattress pad under the fabric for even more lushness. Then we gave it some contrast by putting a bright, bold check on the reproduction chairs."

In an alcove, Gary combines reproductions with antiques and a Swedish bench brightened by a botanical print. "It's simple but wonderful with all of these differently colored woods."

These rooms were decorated especially for this book and are not on display.

*"The furniture is beautifully easy to work with —
and I loved the scale of the sofas. I knew just what
I was going to do as I walked through Craft House."*

A COUNTRY BARN ON LONG ISLAND

"I like to see contrast. That's my philosophy," explains New York City interior designer Mariette Himes Gomez. "I decided to make my country home an example of that with a balance of color and furnishings — a juxta-position of contemporary surroundings with traditional furniture."

Reproduction brass, glass, and furni-ture combine with antique and modern pieces. "The furniture is beautifully easy to work with — and I loved the scale of the sofas. I knew just what I was going to do as I walked through Craft House."

This large room is rich in both detail and imagination. For example, the mantel is made from an old shelf found at a folk art show. The table is a stained *Williamsburg*™ door set on a custom designed base. "I'm very conscious of geometry — of positive and negative space and form," explains Mariette. "But really, you only need good taste and some decorating skills to make a beautiful room."

FURNITURE
USE IN THE EIGHTEENTH CENTURY

Eighteenth-century furniture is not an uncommon sight in the twentieth century. We encounter it at local museums, in antique shops, and, of course, it continues to provide a major design impetus for the furniture industry in the United States. Consequently, most of us are familiar with the various chair and table forms of two centuries past. Yet we often think of these forms in an exclusively twentieth-century context. We view them as the furnishings of our modern homes, environments which, with their comfort and convenience, would have been completely alien to our ancestors. If we reexamine the same antiques from the viewpoint of the colonial householder, there is much to be learned about everyday life two centuries ago.

As an example, consider the portability of eighteenth-century furniture, much of which was designed to be moved frequently. Easy chairs, sofas, bedsteads, and tables of all sorts were frequently fitted with casters, and even large case furniture was sometimes mounted on wheels. Moving parts were also a standard feature of the day. Dining tables normally sported pairs of hinged drop-leaves, while most tea tables and candlestands had tilting tops and card tables could be folded in half.

Though puzzling on the surface, the reasons for this phenomenon are very straightforward. Before the age of electricity, furniture with moving parts allowed the homeowner more options in his or her daily pursuit of necessities such as heat, cool air, and light. In 1750 central heat was still one hundred years away, and the fireplace was the sole means of warming the house. Though dwellings generally had fireplaces in most rooms, it was normally impractical to keep six to ten fires burning twenty-four hours a day. Instead, the practical householder heated only the room

Just as furniture was nestled near the fire in the winter, it was moved to the coolest spot in the house in summer. This was usually the passage, where cross ventilation relieved the mugginess of August in tidewater Virginia. Here the tea table is set for Mrs. Benjamin Powell and her daughters in the passage of their house on Waller Street.

being used at the moment, keeping the door to that space closed in order to retain the warmth. In such situations, it might be so cold in the unheated passageways between rooms that some individuals wore cloaks when going from one part of the house to another, and there are even references to the water in the bedside basin freezing overnight.

That in mind, imagine yourself in your parlor on a cold winter day with a good fire before you. The hour for dinner approaches, but the dining room has been unheated since the previous day. Rather than start a second fire in an attempt to heat the thoroughly chilled dining room for the sake of an hour's meal, you and your family logically take dinner in the already comfortable parlor.

Only now does the desirability of the drop-leaf dining table become clear. With their folding leaves, such tables could fit through doors easily and go from room to room as the need arose. They could even be stored flat against the wall when not in use. Much the same was true for tilt-top tea tables, card tables, and many other forms. And, of course, the casters on the legs of such pieces facilitated movement so that rooms could be reconfigured at will during the day.

English and American housekeepers did, in fact, move some of their furniture on an almost daily basis, taking advantage of existing warmth in winter, seeking cooler spaces and cross breezes in summer, and following the natural light as the sun moved through its course during the day. In short, portability was a very practical response to a genuine need.

These and many other lessons are available to the careful observer of early furniture.
— RONALD L. HURST

Ronald L. Hurst, *curator of furniture, has done considerable research with Virginia probate inventories. He is preparing a book on furniture made in Norfolk, Virginia.*

FURNITURE GLOSSARY

RONALD L. HURST
Curator of Furniture

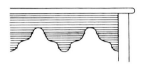

APRON
The plain or shaped framing element that extends between the tops of table legs or at the base of a piece of case furniture.

BLOCK FOOT
A foot, square in cross section, with or without an applied molding.

BOMBÉ
See Swelled Base.

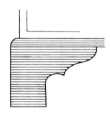

BRACKET FOOT
A foot form used on case furniture that consists of two elements joined at right angles with either a straight or an ogee shape.

CABRIOLE
A leg in the form of a gentle S-curve.

CHAMFER
The beveled edge of an otherwise angular corner, as a Marlborough leg, a bed post, or the corner of a case piece.

COUCH
A long, narrow piece of upholstered seating furniture with no back and a single arm. This form is often called a daybed in the twentieth century.

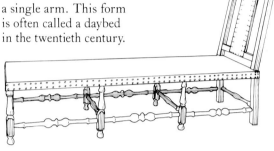

CREST RAIL
The uppermost horizontal element of a chair back.

CROSS BANDING
Wood that has been cut across the grain and veneered for decorative purposes, as on a drawer front.

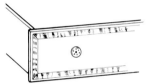

DAYBED
See Couch.

DENTIL COURSE
A series of small, closely set blocks arranged in a row and used as one element in a cornice or other molding.

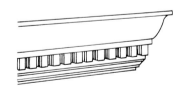

DOVETAIL
A fan-shaped tenon and the mortise into which it fits. Dovetails are often used in rows to join two pieces of wood together tightly.

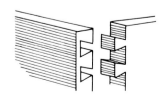

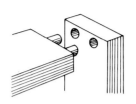

DOWEL
A round wooden pin used to fasten two pieces of wood together. Dowels were not widely employed until the middle of the nineteenth century.

DROP
See Pendant.

EASY CHAIR
A full upholstered armchair with winglike structures projecting forward from the back, designed to catch available heat when turned toward a fireplace.

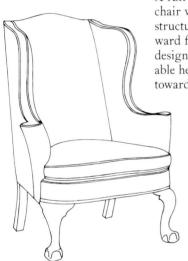

ESCUTCHEON
A surface mounted or inlaid decorative form surrounding a keyhole.

FINIAL
A decorative carved or turned terminal element.

FLUTING
A series of concave vertical grooves used to decorate columns, pilasters, or legs.

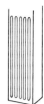

FRETWORK
A carved or sawn interlacing ornament, either cut through or applied to a solid surface.

GADROON
A carved or fluted running molding.

GALLERY
A raised element, pierced or solid, that surrounds the top surface of a piece of furniture.

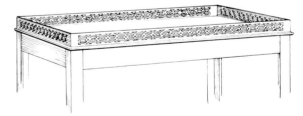

GESSO
A mixture of plaster and glue used for modeling and carving.

GRANDFATHER CLOCK
A term for tall case clock, coined in the 1880s after the publication of a popular song about "Grandfather's Clock." See Tall Case Clock.

GREEK KEY
A classical geometric molding, often in the form of applied fretwork.

INLAY
Pictorial or linear pieces of wood set into the surface of another piece of wood, often of a contrasting color or pattern.

JAPANNING
The use of gesso, paint, and lacquer in Europe or America to simulate East Asian lacquer work.

KNEE
The often curving surface of a leg where it joins the frame of a chair or table.

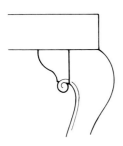

KNEE BLOCK
The plain or ornamental piece of wood that flanks the knee at its joint with the frame.

MORTISE AND TENON
A rectangular cavity (mortise) cut to receive a projecting element (tenon) of the same shape, and used to join two pieces of wood together.

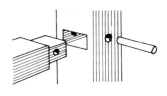

OGEE
A molding or other element with a profile that resembles an S-shape.

PEDIMENT
A triangular or scrolled architectural superstructure, sometimes open in the center (broken pediment).

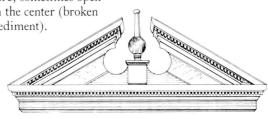

PENDANT
An ornament suspended from the apron of a table or case piece.

SKIRT
See Apron.

SOFA
A long, fully upholstered piece of seating furniture with two arms and a back.

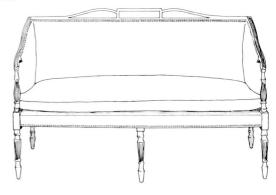

SPLAT
The central element of a chair back.

STRETCHER
The horizontal bracing element between legs.

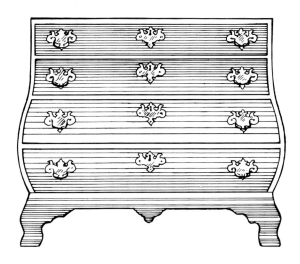

SWELLED
A piece of case furniture that has curvilinear sides is termed "swelled." An ogee bracket foot may carry the same term.

TALL CASE CLOCK
A clock movement fitted in a tall, narrow, wooden case designed to stand on the floor.

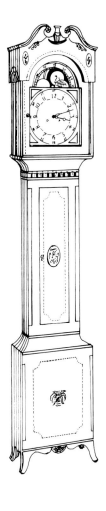

TRIFID FOOT
A carved foot with three projecting lobes.

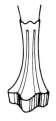

WALL OF TROY
A classical architectural molding, usually in the form of a crenelated wall.

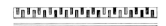

WING CHAIR
See Easy Chair.

CW174

SOFA

Flowing, French-inspired rococo carved scrolls and acanthus leaves often were used to update late baroque style furniture. Here they combine with serpentine curves, cabriole legs, and ball-and-claw feet derived from an Oriental design of a dragon clutching a pearl. This sofa was reproduced from a circa 1760 English antique originally owned by a resident of Newburyport, Massachusetts. Height 35⅞"; Length 88½"; Overall depth 33¼"; Arm height 31". CW174

SOFA

The designs of English cabinet-maker Thomas Chippendale, published in his 1754 *Gentleman and Cabinet-Maker's Director*, contributed greatly to the popularity of the rococo style. The straight, fluted legs on this sofa show the "neat and plain" version of rococo. A reproduction of a circa 1770-1790 English antique, it seats four easily and can be upholstered in your choice of fabric. Height 35"; Length 91"; Overall depth 30"; Arm height: 28¼". CW118

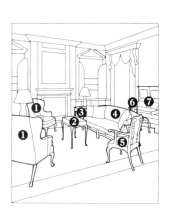

CW118

CW129

SOFA

The symmetry of a long serpentine crest rail and squared Marlborough legs appealed to the colonial taste for simple elegance. The legs were inspired by Chinese furniture, popularized by the burgeoning tea trade, and mark the increasing Chinese influence on design in England and the colonies. Based on a circa 1760-1775 English antique, this reproduction seats three easily and can be upholstered in your choice of leather or fabric.
Height 36"; Length 79"; Overall depth 30½"; Arm height 30¾". CW129

WF1405

SOFA

Inspired by a circa 1750-1770 English rococo antique, this sofa features a serpentine back, scrolled arms, and squared Marlborough-style legs. This style was favored by colonists wealthy enough to afford the luxury of fine furniture.
Height: 36¼"; Length 84"; Overall depth 32½"; Arm height 30½". WF1405

WF1455

SMALL SOFA

This sofa was adapted from the circa 1750-1770 original to accommodate the modern need for smaller but authentic looking period seating. The serpentine back, scrolled arms, and straight legs are without ornamentation, demonstrating English antipathy to the perceived excesses of French rococo designs.
Height 36¼"; Length 61"; Overall depth 32½"; Arm height 30½". WF1455

SETTEE

This small piece shows the strong, symmetrical, yet curvilinear qualities of the late baroque style. As in the circa 1725 English original, this reproduction features carved open S-curved arms terminating in graceful volutes and complemented by sculpted cabriole legs, winglike knee scrolls, and handsome Chinese-inspired pad feet. Height 36¾"; Length 53¾"; Overall depth 29¼"; Arm height 25¾". CW154

CW154

SOFA

The fascination for exotic Oriental motifs generated by trade with the East Indies quickly spread to furniture design. This reproduction of an English circa 1750-1770 antique combines delicately carved Chinese-inspired fretwork on Marlborough legs with the flowing lines and scrolling typical of rococo design. Height 35½"; Length 73"; Overall depth 31½"; Arm height 30". CW23

CW23

CW166

CW44

WF1465

CW166-A

EASY CHAIR

Strikingly modern in its appearance, this late baroque easy chair with its simple cabriole front legs, high pad feet, and squared, flaring rear legs is reproduced from a circa 1750 English antique. The high back and curved sides offered cozy shelter from inhospitable icy winter drafts.
Height 40″; Width 28″; Overall depth 29½″; Arm height 25¼″. CW166

EASY CHAIR

Designed to catch heat when turned toward the fireplace, this reproduction based on a circa 1750 original shows how New England cabinetmakers clung to designs long after they were out of fashion elsewhere. Curved arms, cabriole front legs, and turned stretchers are of late baroque design.
Height 46″; Width 36¾″; Overall depth 33½″ Arm height 25½″. CW44

EASY CHAIR

Inspired by a circa 1730-1740 original, this easy chair has a curved side wing designed to catch heat when the chair is turned toward the fireplace. It is complemented by mahogany cabriole legs and outwardly curved arms typical of the late baroque style.
Height 44½″; Width 28½″; Overall depth 31″; Arm height 26¼″. WF1465

EASY CHAIR

The late baroque's graceful curves, high padded feet, and cabriole front legs are found in this reproduction of a circa 1750 antique. Upholstered in fabric with brass tacks, it offers a comfortable respite from cold winter drafts while pleasing the eye with its simple style.
Height 40″; Width 28″; Overall depth 29½″; Arm height 25¼″. CW166-A

CW163

EASY CHAIR

This reproduction of a circa 1720 English original was made at about the same time that wallpaper was becoming fashionable. Its side wings were designed to catch the heat of the fire while supporting a nodding head. This chair exemplifies the late baroque style that began at the end of Queen Anne's reign and continued well into the reign of George III. Gracefully curved arms, carved front cabriole legs accented by a beaded edge outlining the knee, and S-shaped rear legs are distinctive features of the late baroque. This chair can be upholstered in your choice of fabric or leather.
Height 49″; Width 32½″; Overall depth 32¼″; Arm height 26¼″. CW163

WF 1412

WF 1447

CW 12

CW 104

EASY CHAIR

Inspired by a New England antique circa 1760-1790, this chair features the side wings, serpentine shape, and straight, sturdy looking legs that often characterize late rococo design in the eighteenth century. At the same time, it offers extra padding for modern comfort.
Height 45"; Width 32"; Overall depth 32"; Arm height 24".
WF 1412

EASY CHAIR

The design of this easy chair was inspired by the beautifully pro-portioned wings, rolled arms, and, in the tapered legs, a hint of the neoclassic style often associated with Hepplewhite and Sheraton. The original was made in En-gland circa 1775-1790 and very likely was placed by the fireplace in the bedchamber.
Height 45"; Width 29"; Overall depth 28"; Arm height 27½".
WF 1447

EASY CHAIR

Stop-fluted Marlborough legs and durable, curled hair filler under the upholstery were preva-lent in easy chairs such as this one made by a Newport, Rhode Island, cabinetmaker circa 1750-1775. This reproduction employs both features and offers the option for upholstering in your choice of fabric or leather.
Height 45½"; Width 31"; Overall depth 28"; Arm height 25½".
CW 12

EASY CHAIR

In 1745, as the British took the Fortress of Louisbourg in Nova Scotia and began driving the French from North America, col-onists were settled comfortably in English easy chairs such as this. This reproduction of an original circa 1745 features ball-and-claw feet with elegantly carved acan-thus leaves on the knees. It can be upholstered in your choice of fab-ric or leather.
Height 44"; Width 33"; Overall depth 31½"; Arm height 26".
CW 104

CW305

EASY CHAIR

The popularity of the easy chair began to fade in both Europe and the colonies concurrent with the rise of neoclassicism. This style, resulting from public interest in the excavation of Pompeii and Her-culaneum, led Thomas Chippendale to begin designing neoclassic furniture to fit new houses designed by architects such as Robert Adam. Based on a circa 1790 antique chair made in Baltimore, this reproduction uses handsome front and side boxwood bands and leg inlay to lighten the heavier lines of the mahogany.
Height 44½"; Width 31¾"; Overall depth 33"; Arm height 26½".
CW305

CW304

CW128

WF1446

WF1456

CHAIR

Neoclassicism was embraced fervently in post-Revolutionary Virginia. The architecture of Monticello, the University of Virginia, and neighboring Washington, D. C., featured the same clean lines and refined styling as furniture of the period. This reproduction of a circa 1800 American chair with padded arms can be upholstered in your choice of fabric or leather.
Height 44¼"; Width 28¼"; Overall depth 26½"; Arm height 25". CW304

BACK STOOL

With the growing demand for furniture that was not only functional but also comfortable, the "back stool" appeared in the late baroque period: a chair with both upholstered seat and back. This reproduction of a circa 1740 English antique with its graceful cabriole legs and pad feet can be upholstered in your choice of fabric or leather.
Height 38½"; Width 23¼"; Overall depth 23". CW128

BACK STOOL

This particular back stool is based on an antique made in New England circa 1760-1775. It features the serpentine crest rail and handsome proportions of the original, and can be upholstered in your choice of fabric or leather.
Height: 37¾"; Width 22¾"; Overall depth 23½". WF1446

OPEN ARM CHAIR

Adapted from a New England back stool made circa 1760-1775, this side chair features the serpentine crest rail characteristic of the late baroque period. The proportions of this adaptation are slightly wider and deeper to balance the addition of the arms. The arms, seat, and back can be upholstered in your choice of fabric or leather.
Height 37¾"; Width 24½"; Overall depth 25½"; Arm height 26". WF1456

CW67

SIDE CHAIR

This reproduction of an English antique circa 1725 is an excellent example of the emphasis on shaping and symmetry in the late baroque period. The original, with its cabriole leg C-scrolls, rich gold-leaf shell and bellflower motifs, and curled hair under upholstery, may well have seated London opera goers in their parlors as they discussed the premiere of Handel's "Rodelinde." In the colonies, such chairs were found in homes of the well-to-do.
Height 41½"; Width 22¼"; Overall depth 24¼". CW67

OPEN ARM CHAIR

This rococo design open arm chair was inspired by a circa 1765-1790 New England original. The raked back, padded arms, and deep seat offer comfort balanced by style: a serpentine crest rail, straight Marlborough legs in front, and squared, slightly swept back rear legs. Height 43½″; Width 27¾″; Overall depth 27¼″; Arm height 27¼″. WF1425

OPEN ARM CHAIR

Demonstrating the eighteenth-century taste for the "neat and plain" version of rococo furniture design, this open arm chair is inspired by the squared Marlborough legs and curved arm supports of an English circa 1750-1765 original. Many colonists during this period could not afford such lavish, fully uphol-stered furniture. Height 39″; Width 24″; Overall depth 27¼″; Arm height 24¾″. WF1411

In the ceremonial upper chamber of the governor's house where Lord Botetourt met with his Council and other dignitaries, he kept nine "crimson damask chairs."

WF1425

WF1411

OPEN ARM CHAIR

With the publication of the excavations at Herculaneum in 1748 came a growing interest in ancient Roman design, as demonstrated here. Known as a lolling chair, this mahogany reproduction of a circa 1790 New England original shows tapered legs and new emphasis on flat surfaces and boxwood line inlay. The use of classical motifs and simple symmetrical lines illustrates in smaller scale the neoclassic style in domestic interiors rather than monuments. Height 48″; Width 26″; Overall depth 26½″; Arm height 28″. CW13

OPEN ARM CHAIR

In the eighteenth century, the most comfortable furniture was usually reserved for the bedchamber or parlor. Inspired by a New England antique circa 1770-1790, this open arm chair combines both practical comfort and traditional design elements. It blends late baroque and rococo styles into a delicately designed chair with straight Marlborough legs, serpentine curved back, and carved arms terminating in volutes. Height 41″; Width 27½″; Overall depth 22¾″; Arm height 24¾″. WF1440

OPEN ARM CHAIR

This neoclassical design has been reproduced from a Massachusetts original circa 1800. The light, clean lines so popular in post-Revolutionary America and during the reigns of George III and IV in England contrast with the more ornate rococo designs that preceded the neoclassic period. This chair is available for upholstery in your choice of fabric or leather. Height 43⅝″; Width 25⅞″; Overall depth 27″; Arm height 26⅜″. CW307

CW13

WF1440

CW307

CW136

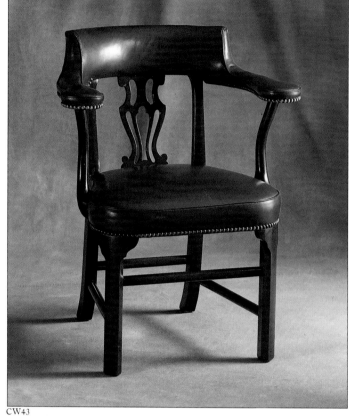

CW43

CORNER CHAIR

Also known as a smoking chair and often used at a desk or writing table, this reproduction corner chair is based on an antique made in Philadelphia circa 1750. Its turned stiles and baluster shaped solid back splats are typical of the late baroque style. It is available for upholstery in your choice of fabric or leather.
Height 31¼"; Width 26"; Overall depth 26"; Arm height 29¾". CW136

ARM CHAIR

An eighteenth-century gentleman could often be found with long clay pipe in hand, seated at a desk or writing table, occasionally in a chair such as this. A comfortable chair, with continuous crest rail and padded back, arms, and seat, this unusual rococo design has been reproduced from an English circa 1760 original. It is available for upholstery in your choice of fabric or leather.
Height 34"; Width 29"; Overall depth 24½"; Arm height 29½".
CW43

CW185

BENCH

This neoclassic bench is reproduced from an English antique circa 1790. A serpentine front rail and tapered legs enhance this simple piece, often used as a window seat. It is available for upholstery in your choice of fabric.
Height 17½"; Length 32⅝"; Width 14⅛". CW185

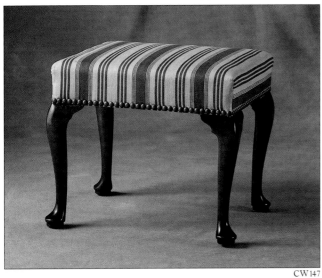

CW 147

Thomas Everard, clerk of the York County Court, was a prosperous widower in 1770. The decoration and furnishings of his chamber — wallpaper, window curtains, mahogany high-post bedstead, clothespress, footstools — illustrate his comfortable situation.

STOOL

This light, graceful design is reproduced in mahogany from an English antique circa 1740. It features full nail trim and upholstery over the rails, as well as the cabriole legs and pad feet typical of the late baroque period. Height 17″; Width 21½″; Length 17″. CW 147

WINDSOR BENCH

Adapted from a seven-foot-long New England original circa 1790-1840, this Windsor bench was less common than chairs of the same design. This reproduction uses a single pine board for the seat, oak or ash for the spindles, and maple for the legs. Height 38″; Width 53″; Overall depth 21½″; Arm height 27″. 2014AP

2014AP

CW 16   CW 16-A

SIDE/ARM CHAIR

The interlaced strapwork of the splat exemplifies what Chippendale called the "modern" or French rococo style. Curved, flowing arms terminating in delicate carving add to the grace of this design, reproduced from an English antique circa 1765. It may be upholstered in your choice of fabric or leather.

Side chair: Height 37¼"; Width 22"; Overall depth 21½". CW 16

Arm chair: Height 37¼"; Width 24"; Overall depth 21½"; Arm height 27⅝". CW 16-A

WF3371   WF3370

SIDE/ARM CHAIR

Inspired by a Maryland antique circa 1760-1780, this mahogany chair features a carved, pierced back splat characteristic of rococo styling. Mahogany, imported from the West Indies in the eighteenth century, offers a dense grain that facilitates the finely carved detail in the arms and back.

Side chair: Height 38"; Width 21"; Overall depth 20¼". WF3370

Arm chair: Height 38"; Width 26½"; Overall depth 21¼"; Arm height 27". WF3371

SIDE/ARM CHAIR

Inspired by a Philadelphia late baroque/rococo design circa 1760-1770, this mahogany chair features volute carved ears and a handsome, solid, vase-shaped splat. The ball-and-claw feet are a common feature of American rococo furniture. Chairs such as these were usually purchased in multiples of six or sets of twelve. When not in use, they stood against the walls of the dining room, bedchamber, parlor, or passage. They were arranged as needed for meetings, meals, musical performances, games, or other entertainment. Both the side and arm chairs are available for upholstering in your choice of fabric or leather.

Side chair: Height 38¼″; Width 21¼″; Overall depth 21″. WF3303

Arm chair: Height 38¼″; Width 28″; Overall depth 23″; Arm height 26¼″. WF3304

WF3304

WF3303

CW142-A   CW142

SIDE/ARM CHAIR

The demand for comfort prompted the design of a more contoured chair back in the early eighteenth century. This late baroque chair reveals an Oriental influence resulting from the exposure of Western cabinetmakers to tea trade imports. This influence is expressed in pad feet and broad, sweeping curves. Refined scroll carving flanks each knee. The side chair is reproduced from an English antique circa 1740. The arm chair is an adaptation of this same original, widened to balance the sweep of the arms. The seat frame is fitted with a slip seat and may be ordered with muslin or leather over curled hair filling.
Side chair: Height 40½"; Width 21¼"; Overall depth 20½".
CW142
Arm chair: Height 40½"; Width 24"; Overall depth 20½"; Arm height 27½". CW142-A

The curvilinear style of these chairs and the double-domed desk and bookcase was old fashioned by the 1770s, so Peyton and Betty Randolph relegated them to a work area, called "Mrs. Randolph's closet" in the household estate inventory.

CW 151

ARM CHAIR

This late baroque chair was reproduced from an English original circa 1740. Its cabriole legs, voluted arms, and solid contoured back splat shaped like beaked birds facing an urn contribute to this chair's flowing lines and graceful design.
Height 39¾"; Width 28"; Overall depth 23½"; Arm height 27¼". CW 151

SIDE CHAIR

Reproduced from a Philadelphia antique circa 1750, this elaborately detailed solid mahogany chair is typical of the curvilinear late baroque style. The serpentine crest rail features a naturalistic scallop shell, a form of ornamentation echoed by a shell on each knee of the cabriole legs. A cone and heart design pierces the curved splat back. The seat may be upholstered in your choice of fabric.
Height 43¼"; Width 20¼"; Overall depth 20". CW 146

CW 146

WF3319   WF3318

SIDE/ARM CHAIR

Inspired by a "neat and plain" side chair made in Virginia circa 1760-1780, this mahogany chair features the elegant details that typify the work of this period's southern cabinetmakers. Straight legs are a serene counterpoint to the simply pierced back splat. During this period in Virginia planter society, dances were especially popular. Chairs such as this would have been pushed back against the walls of the hall, parlor, or ballroom, leaving space to dance.

Side chair: Height 37½"; Width 21"; Overall depth 20". WF3318
Arm chair: Height 37½"; Width 25"; Overall depth 21¼"; Arm height 27¼". WF3319

CW47-1   CW47

SIDE/ARM CHAIR

The original of this late eighteenth-century reproduction was made in England circa 1775. It blends late baroque details with the rococo "modern" style popular in this period. A mahogany back splat features woven strapwork. Arms curve gently into a lightly curled scroll.

Side chair: Height 37¾"; Width 22¼"; Overall depth 22". CW47-1
Arm chair: Height 37¾"; Width 26"; Overall depth 22½"; Arm height 27". CW47

CW 17   CW 17-A

Side/Arm Chair

Fluid rococo lines form interlacing mahogany ribbons to
support the back in comfort
and in beauty. Reproduced
from a Philadelphia antique
circa 1780, this side chair's
molded front legs with chamfered inside corner, swept
back rear legs, and serpentine
curved front rail create a
light, graceful design. The
arm chair was adapted from
the same original. George
Washington acquired chairs
of a similar design during his
tenure in Philadelphia.
Side chair: Height 37½";
Width 22½"; Overall depth
23¾". CW 17
Arm chair: Height 37½";
Width 25"; Overall depth
24½"; Arm height 26¾".
CW 17-A

2014P

Windsor Chair

This bow-back Windsor
chair, adapted from a Rhode
Island original circa 1780-
1800, has been slightly
altered in its height and seat
width for greater comfort.
English Windsors tended to
have a thin elm seat devoid of
shaping. In contrast, American Windsors had a thick,
deeply shaped, far more comfortable seat. In this chair
design, ash, maple, and pine
combine with mahogany
arms. The bow back is made
by steaming the straight crest
rail into a sharp curve. Arms
are attached directly to the
bow.
Height 39"; Width 21½";
Overall depth 20"; Arm
height 25". 2014P

CW33

CW34

DINING TABLE/END SECTION

As the eighteenth century progressed, wealthy English and American families began adopting the French idea of designating a room strictly for dining, replacing the previous custom of using a "hall" for eating, entertaining, working, and sleeping. In these new rooms, multi-course meals were served that were rich in variety, quantity, and conversation. Drop-leaf tables accommodated inevitable extra guests. The table ends could be detached and stored against the walls or used as additional serving tables.

This reproduction of an English table made about 1760 is a prime example of the flexibility of eighteenth-century dining tables. Barely two feet long when closed, the drop leaves open to five and one-half feet. Combined with the two end sections, the table is nine and one-half feet long. The end sections can also be locked together to form a more intimate but still generous round table. All are made of mahogany, with Chinese-inspired Marlborough legs and simple rococo lines. Dining table: Height 29¼"; Width 48"; Length 22" closed, 67" open. CW33
End section: Height 29¼"; Width 48"; Depth 23½". CW34

In the 1750s, following the English and Virginia trend for building spacious rooms where large groups might gather (assembly rooms), Peyton Randolph added a large dining room to the house he had inherited from his father. The expensively furnished room contained four large looking glasses, two dining tables, one sideboard table, one marble table, and a dozen mahogany chairs.

CW34 Two END SECTIONS, page 78; CW47 SIDE CHAIRS, page 76.

CW66

CW65

DINING TABLE

This mahogany pedestal base dining table ensemble is based on a Colonial Revival adaptation. The original late nineteenth-century table combines the pedestal form popular about 1820 with the late baroque style of the early eighteenth century. This configuration can employ the end sections separately as serving tables, together as a dining table, and, for larger gatherings, together with individual two-foot-wide leaves, or with one or more pedestal center sections. Tilting tops allow each pedestal section to be stored neatly against the wall.

Center section: Height 28½";
Width 48"; Length 32½". CW65
End section: Height 28½";
Width 48"; Length 33¼". CW66

CW66 Two END SECTIONS, CW65 CENTER SECTION

WF3243

DINING TABLE

English visitors in America in the early nineteenth century often were astounded at the abundance set before them at dinner. More than simply being invited to eat, they were pressed to feast both on fine food and drink as well as to enjoy convivial company. With dining often the center of social life, Americans developed the habit of being prepared for company. In earlier times, rooms served multiple purposes and dropleaf tables often were pushed against the wall when not in actual use. By the 1820s, a room had been designated primarily for dining only, not combined with the card playing, schooling, business, or even nursing as in the century before. This pedestal table was created to be left standing in the middle of the dining room at all times. It was inspired by an American neoclassic piece made about 1820. The original design has been modified slightly to accommodate the scale of modern rooms as well as to increase the comfort and stability of the table itself. Castors on brass paw feet make it easier to move.

Two end sections with center section and two 18″ leaves: Height 29½″; Width 46″; Length 144″. WF3244

Two end sections with two 18″ leaves: Height 29½″; Width 46″; Length 72″. WF3243

The governor had the best stocked wine cellar in the colony, so he could entertain his guests with fine Madeira or a hearty punch.

CW 117

DINING TABLE

In 1730, at about the same time Benjamin Franklin published *Poor Richard's Almanack*, the original of this oval gateleg table was made in England. It is influenced by both Chinese and European styles. It features carved shell and pendant bellflowers enhancing cabriole legs. Typically, these legs are attached to the rails in such a way as to swing like gates, snug into the frame, allowing the leaves to be left up for dining or down vertically for compact storage against the wall.

Height 29″; Width 58″; Length 24″ closed, 70″ open. CW 117

CW177

DINING TABLE

Before central heating, family meals often were served before the fireplace in winter and in the coolest location of the house in summer. Tables were designed to be portable and store compactly. The original of this neoclassic reproduction was made in Boston circa 1810. Two gates are supported by tapered columnar posts and splayed legs with brass paw feet and casters. Elegantly simple but extensive reeding appears in the edge of the top, the lower edge of the apron, the posts, and upper face of the legs.
Drop-leaf Dining Table
Height 28½";
Closed 56½" × 14¾";
Open 56½" × 66⅝". CW177

Portable furniture and household servants allowed eighteenth-century rooms to serve many functions. Dining tables, for instance, were folded down and put back against the wall between meals; the dining room could then serve as a family sitting area or even study.

WF3240

DINING TABLE

By the early part of the nineteenth century, the population in America exceeded seven million. Dining was a major pastime, especially in the homes of the urban well-to-do. Entire afternoons would be spent over rich, multi-course dinners. Dancing and card playing well into the night were followed by a late supper. This dining table is inspired by an American original circa 1800-1820. Turned columns top gracefully splayed supports tapering into brass encased feet. The pedestal design was originally intended for tables that would stand permanently in the center of the dining room, but multiple pieces add flexibility to this notion. Each end piece may be used as a console, serving table, or placed against the wall. Eighteen-inch leaves can extend the length of the assembled dining table. Extra leaves can expand its length.
Height 29½″; Width 48″; Length 108″ with two 18″ leaves, 72″ without leaves. WF3240

TABLE

This trestle style reproduction of an eighteenth-century New England antique might have had a fairly prominent position in a simple household, or have appeared in the work areas of a wealthy household. Simple construction suggests crafting by a joiner, not a cabinetmaker. Like the original, this reproduction features top and batten ends of white pine, with all other elements of maple. Available in three lengths.
Height 29″; Width 30″; Length 42″. 3014X
Height 29″; Width 30″; Length 58″. 3114X
Height 29″; Width 30″; Length 74″. 3214X

3014X

WF3240 TABLE, page 84; 2014P WINDSOR CHAIRS, page 77.

WF3841

SIDEBOARD

As households grew more affluent and wealth came to be measured by possessions rather than landholdings, storage became an important consideration. Traditional serving tables evolved into sideboards: serving areas plus storage and display space. This evolution took place primarily in the late eighteenth century and was fostered by furniture designers such as George Hepplewhite and Thomas Sheraton. Inspired by a Virginia or North Carolina original circa 1790-1810, this neoclassic style sideboard reflects simple elegance and grace with an underlying practical sturdiness. It features oval brasses, one partitioned drawer for silver, and two deep cabinets for stacking plates.
Height 39¾"; Length 56½"; Depth 24". WF3841

CW87

SIDEBOARD

As wealth increased in the colonies, families began to acquire more specialized dining utensils in greater quantities. In addition to standard place settings, there were many serving pieces for leisurely, multi-course eighteenth-century meals. Easy access and secure storage became important considerations for which the sideboard was an ideal solution. This reproduction of a late eighteenth- or early nineteenth-century Virginia or North Carolina sideboard is made of mahogany. The graceful arch in the center panel is typical of the more intimate, scaled down use of architectural forms in the neoclassic style. Slender, tapering legs, cock beading at the drawer edges, and octagonal key escutcheons add interest without detracting from the clean, elegant form.
Height 40½"; Length 57"; Depth 20¼". CW87

CW300

SIDEBOARD

Exquisite inlay demonstrates the neoclassical craftsman's ability to convey a richness of detail on flat surfaces. This reproduction copies a Charleston, South Carolina, sideboard circa 1800. It features husks, flutes, and paterae meticulously inlaid in holly against a finely grained mahogany ground. Shapes are reprised in delightfully unexpected ways: the oval inlays are echoed by oval brasses and tapering legs end in daintily tapering block feet. A deep drawer and large cupboard provide ample storage space for dishes and serving pieces while a removable wood tray with lined insert in the center drawer offers a place to store flatware.

Height 36"; Length 72"; Depth 27⅝". CW300

SIDEBOARD

This mahogany sideboard is inspired by an English antique circa 1800 at Bassett Hall, the Williamsburg home of Mr. and Mrs. John D. Rockefeller, Jr. Elegant neoclassic styling is reflected in the delicately bowed front, graceful arch, stamped brasses, line inlay, and beading outlining the doors.

Height 36½"; Length 53"; Depth 23¾". WF3845

WF3845

CW148

SIDEBOARD

The term "sideboard" came into use around 1780, about the time when side tables increased in height and began to feature storage compartments. Its predecessor was used for dressing food in the kitchen and consequently was known as a "dresser" in the early eighteenth century. This particular piece is a reproduction of an English original circa 1740. Its style is late baroque, featuring a handsomely carved apron, paneled sides, and drawers beautifully bordered in crossbanded mahogany. A refined cabriole leg curves into delicate pad feet. Custom made oval brass knobs with a nickel silver insert through the center are complemented by unusually shaped brass escutcheons.
Height 33¾"; Length 77½"; Depth 21¼". CW148

CABINET

Reproduced from an English metal lined plate warmer circa 1765, this cabinet makes an unusual bar, storage, or service piece. The paneled door, bracket feet, and simple brassware exemplify the "neat and plain" version of rococo styling. Originally, the interior held warmed plates to help food retain its heat after being carried from the kitchen to the dining room. Two top flaps fold out for serving.
Height 36⅞" open, 37⅝" closed; Width 37¼" open, 18⅝" closed; Depth 19⅜". CW186

CW186

The marble slab table in the governor's dining room sparkles with Lord Botetourt's cut wine glasses and decanters.

SIDEBOARD TABLE

A predecessor to more elaborate sideboards made later in the century, this reproduction of a New England late baroque sideboard table circa 1745-1770 reflects the influence of Britain's Augustan age. Mahogany and easy-to-maintain marble carry out the taste for rich surfaces. The serpentine apron is supported by gently curving cabriole legs with shell carvings adorning the front knees and apron.
Height 27½"; Length 52⅛"; Depth 24". CW155

SIDEBOARD TABLE

Inspired by a sideboard table made in Williamsburg, Virginia, circa 1750-1770, this form was used as the principal serving point in an era before the later development of the sideboard. Its simple yet fluid lines feature winged brasses, cabriole legs, and orientally derived high pad feet, all characteristic of Virginia cabinetry of the period.
Height 29¼"; Width 46"; Depth 22". WF1269

CW155

WF1269

Lord Botetourt's butler, Marshman, safe-guarded the palace silver, glassware, and spirits from his pantry domain.

WF3568

SILVER CHEST

Tools were such a valuable commodity in the eighteenth century that even gentlemen sometimes maintained their own personal tool sets. In such cases, a mahogany chest such as this was provided for storage of tools within the home. This chest was inspired by an English rococo tool chest circa 1770. Simple lines and delicate scale make it ideal for storage of silver or flatware in modern homes.
Height 35⅞"; Width 24⅞"; Depth 12⅝". WF3568

BREAKFRONT BOOKCASE

In 1455, Johannes Gutenberg, in partnership with a wealthy gold-smith named Johann Fust, established at Mainz a press using movable type. Within fifty years, over 1,000 printing companies produced 10,000,000 copies of 35,000 books.

Books still were relatively scarce in the eighteenth century but men of wealth and education, such as Virginia's Peyton Randolph, president of the First Continental Congress, often had extensive libraries. His books, with their leather covers, fragile bindings, and furtive glues, were stored in six large "bookpresses." His cousin, Thomas Jefferson, bought this library and later sold it to the United States government as the nucleus of the Library of Congress.

This magnificent mahogany reproduction of a circa 1750 English rococo bookpress is ample demonstration of its owner's wealth and education. It has robust brasses and a handsomely carved pediment. Oriental influence is apparent in its glass panel configuration, combined with a hint of neoclassicism in the Greek key scrollwork.
Height 95⅞"; Width 71½"; Depth 18¾". CW158

WF3709

BREAKFRONT BOOKCASE

This design is inspired by a Massachusetts original circa 1810-1820. It shows a strong Gothic influence held over from rococo, but with the lighter suggestion of neoclassicism. The tall Gothic arches framing glazed doors originally might have had curtains to keep sunlight from damaging the valued books stored inside. Today, an optional spotlight and framed glass shelves make an ideal environment for displaying china, crystal, or other fine objects. Height 87¼"; Length 61¾"; Depth 17⅜". WF3702

Peyton Randolph, speaker of the House of Burgesses, owned an extensive legal library that was housed in six mahogany bookpresses. His books passed to his cousin, Thomas Jefferson, who eventually sold them at a loss to the United States government to form the nucleus of the Library of Congress.

BREAKFRONT BOOKCASE

This sturdy piece of furniture was reproduced from an English oak original circa 1750, about the same time that Benjamin Franklin received an honorary Master of Arts degree from the College of William and Mary in Williamsburg. Bookcases usually were owned by well-educated individuals as a place to store valued books and documents. This particular example features a high molded cornice with a border of sawn dentils at the top. Glazed paneled doors enclose the top section while solid paneled doors enclose the bottom. The entire piece is supported by four bracket feet. Height 89½"; Width 55¼"; Depth 22¼". WF3709

Bombé Chest-on-Chest

This magnificent reproduction is based on a circa 1780 antique made in coastal Massachusetts, probably along Boston's north shore. Also known as a "kettle-base" design, bombé furniture was produced only in this area of the colonies and is an interesting revival of the late baroque affection for bulbous shapes. As in the original, this chest is constructed of 265 pieces of fine mahogany and, as a secondary wood, white pine. Sand-cast brasses echo the unusual carvings on the pediment of this piece along with the moldings at the cornice, capitals, and waist. The scroll top, handsomely turned finial, and shell design are all typical of the late baroque, as is the ogee curved bracket foot. Each reproduction of this meticulously crafted chest includes a document of origin signed by the cabinetmaker. Height 91¾"; Width 46"; Depth 23⅞". CW190

CW19

Dressing Table

Intricate carving distinguishes this mahogany reproduction of a rococo Pennsylvania dressing table circa 1760. Originally, this piece would have been used in a bedroom to hold clothing and toiletries, a task for which it is superbly suited today. The case features fluted quarter columns and bold brass hardware, while the sturdy cabriole legs are adorned with acanthus leaf carving and carved ball-and-claw feet. Acanthus is a genus of plants and shrubs found in the tropics and southern Europe. This motif often was used by the Greeks for the capitals of Corinthian columns.
Height 32"; Length 38½"; Depth 20". CW19

WF2662

CW153

HIGH CHEST OF DRAWERS

The deeply stepped center ogee on the skirt of this high chest is flanked by shallow ogees and accented by handsomely turned acorn drops. All are hallmarks of the late baroque. Inspired by a Massachusetts original made circa 1725-1750, this high chest of drawers features gracefully tall cabriole legs, locking hardware on graduated drawers, and the warmth of mahogany.
Height 63¼"; Width 40⅜"; Depth 21¾". WF2662

HIGH CHEST OF DRAWERS

About 1760, during the time that political discontent with England was spreading throughout the colonies, the original of this commodious chest was made in New Jersey. The closely grained mahogany of this reproduction is well suited for the creation of the boldly scalloped skirt and graceful cabriole legs with carved ball-and-claw feet. Bail and rosette brasses in the neoclassic style update the basically late baroque form.
Height 69¾"; Width 42¾"; Depth 22⅞". CW153

CW 191

CHEST OF DRAWERS

Reproduced from a Charleston, South Carolina, chest circa 1780, this meticulously crafted neoclassic design features a gracefully carved and curved serpentine front framed by canted corners, a robustly shaped top, and bracket feet. Inlaid stringing delineates the feet and hand-fitted drawer corners as well as the crotch-grained mahogany drawers book-matched to the solid mahogany front. Flat surfaces are inlaid with husks, paterae, and rosettes. The interior wood is yellow pine.
Height 34 1/16"; Width 41 9/16"; Depth 24 5/16". CW 191

The original Charleston-made chest of drawers is displayed in the Masterworks Gallery of the DeWitt Wallace Decorative Arts Gallery.

CW 176

CHEST OF DRAWERS

In 1770, the mania for furniture with Oriental overtones was still in full swing and probably was the motivating force behind the delicate hand-sawn fretwork adorning the chamfered corners of this mahogany chest. This fretwork is an exotic counterpoint to the French-inspired serpentine rococo front and unusual three-sided bracket feet. This reproduction of a circa 1770 Philadelphia chest features generously proportioned graduated drawers, each with its own lock. The large scale of this piece is typical of the work of Philadelphia cabinetmakers during this period. Chests of such scale also may have been used in dining rooms.
Height 33½"; Width 44¼"; Depth 23". CW 176

CHEST OF DRAWERS

The original of this reproduction chest was made in
Massachusetts between 1760
and 1770. Serpentine curves
and high bracket feet typify
rococo styling. Graduated
drawers hold an ample inventory of clothing, linens, or
other items.
Height 31¾"; Width 37⅞";
Depth 21⅞". CW 183

CHEST OF DRAWERS

Originally made in Pennsylvania circa 1770, this quietly
elegant reproduction chest
features superb detailing:
beading around each drawer
front, handsomely propor-
tioned bracket feet, delicately
fluted quarter columns, and
graceful brass escutcheons
and drawer pulls. Complex
joinery with precise dove-
tailing is reproduced
meticulously on the inside.
Graduated drawers are generous in volume and, in the
original, may have held
clothing.
Height 35½"; Width 38¼";
Depth 19½". CW 18

*A "large walnut chest of draws"
in Lord Botetourt's bedchamber
at the palace held "Linen,
Gloves, Stockings & C" —
the elements of proper gentle-
manly attire.*

CW 183

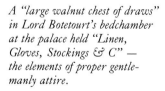

CW 18

99

CW68

CHEST OF DRAWERS

Reproduced from an English original circa 1740, this chest was built in a desirable small size in the late baroque style. Handsome brasses and fine grained mahogany offer simple lines and versatility. The top slides out for use as a writing surface or dressing table. Graduated drawers increase in size from top to bottom. Side handles facilitate portability, an important consideration for eighteenth-century householders. Height 29¾"; Width 30"; Depth 17½". CW68

WF2602

CHEST OF DRAWERS

This straightforward, "neat and plain" version of a rococo style chest was inspired by an original made in eastern Virginia circa 1775. It features high bracket feet and gracefully simple brasses. Because eighteenth-century homes did not always contain closets, the graduated drawers in this chest, including two smaller drawers on top, were ideal for organizing and storing a wide range of clothing such as stockings and breeches, or petticoats and shifts.
Height 35¼"; Width 37½"; Depth 21¾". WF2602

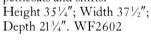

CHEST OF DRAWERS

Inspired by an English rococo chest circa 1750-1770, this small chest presents features of value to an eighteenth-century man. A pull-out shelf turns it into a desk, writing table, or dressing table. Side brasses aid portability. Finely grained mahogany and "neat and plain" rococo styling also make this chest as handsome as it is practical.
Height 30½"; Width 31¼"; Depth 18". WF2531

CHEST OF DRAWERS

This chest of drawers was inspired by a Valley of Virginia antique circa 1770-1790. This adaptation is made of mahogany and exemplifies the colonial preference for the "neat and plain" version of rococo design rather than highly ornamented, French-inspired creations. Subtly graduated drawers, bracket feet, and elegant brasswork combine for gracious proportions and commodious storage capacity.
Height 46½"; Width 40"; Depth 20". WF2608

Lord Botetourt has left his walking stick, watch, and gloves on top of the chest of drawers in this chamber. The bedstead is fitted out with its summer hangings of silk gauze mosquito curtains.

WF2531

WF2608

CW139-S

BEDSTEAD

The original of this solid mahogany reproduction high-post bedstead was made in New England circa 1760-1775 and probably provided a place of refuge to its owner from the political unrest and turbulence engulfing the colonies. This bedstead features some details generally found in the late baroque style. Cabriole legs taper to ball-and-claw feet carved in the New England style. A simple, arched headboard and gracefully tapering headposts attest to rococo influence and are topped by a flat tester. Curtains at the head and foot kept warmth in, insects out, and protected the sleeper from drafts.

Queen: Width 68½"; Height 87¾"; Length 88¼". CW139-60

Double: Width 61½"; Height 87¾"; Length 82¼". CW139

Single: Width 46½"; Height 87¾"; Length 82¼". CW139-S

WF2022

WF2011

HALF- AND FULL-TESTER BEDSTEADS

This bedstead is inspired by a half-tester New England antique circa 1790-1810. This particular bed features simple tapered posts and a flat headboard. Unlike its forebear that came equipped with rope to support a mattress stuffed with horsehair or feathers, this bed comes fitted for a standard mattress and box spring.

Queen: Height $79\frac{1}{2}''$; Width $63\frac{1}{2}''$; Length $85\frac{1}{2}''$.
Double: Height $79\frac{1}{2}''$; Width $56\frac{1}{2}''$; Length $79\frac{5}{8}''$.
Single: Height $79\frac{1}{2}''$; Width $41\frac{1}{2}''$; Length $79\frac{5}{8}''$.

Full-tester:
Queen: WF2022
Double: WF2012
Single: WF2002

Half-tester:
Queen: WF2021
Double: WF2011
Single: WF2001

WILLIAM AND MARY COVERLET AND BEDSPREAD

The border of this coverlet is taken from an original hand-quilted late seventeenth-century Portuguese or Indian quilt that features a remarkable border design of bird, animal, and plant motifs. The reproduction has a diamond pattern center. It is reproduced in 100 percent cotton using a complex matelasse weave on a jacquard loom. On a standard size bed, the bedspread reaches the floor. To use as a coverlet, order the next smallest size.

		Antique White	White
Queen	102″ × 116″	7802-WH04	7802-WH61
Full	96″ × 110″	7802-WH04	7802-WH61
Twin	80″ × 110″	7802-WH04	7802-WH61

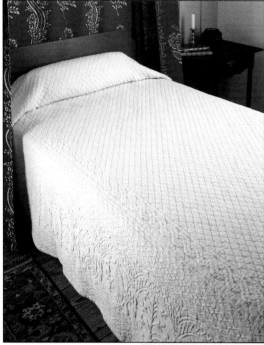

WILLIAM AND MARY COVERLET

The bedstead in the chamber over the dining room at the Palace has hangings and covered cornice of a copper-plate-printed fabric in the purple and green color scheme popular with many of Thomas Chippendale's patrons.

LOW-POST BEDSTEAD

What beds in the early colonies lacked in comfort they made up for in ingenuity. One- and two-room houses often had "press" beds, a kind of Murphy bed that folded to the wall to create floorspace. As the colonies grew, pure functionalism gave way to comfort and fashionability. This low-post bed is inspired by a Newport, Rhode Island, antique circa 1760-1790. It features a delicately curved mahogany headboard and deep fluting on the posts, typical of the work of Newport craftsmen such as the Townsends and the Goddards.

Queen: Height 40¼″; Width 64¼″; Length 85½″. WF2023

Double: Height 40½″; Width 56½″; Length 79½″. WF2013

Single: Height 40¼″; Width 41½″; Length 79½″ WF2003

WF2003

BEDSTEAD

As the eighteenth century drew to a close, Americans could sleep easier knowing that certain freedoms were guaranteed by the Bill of Rights. At about this time, the original of this New England circa 1790-1810 bedstead was made. The arched tester was originally associated with military furniture and, as a result, this design is known as a "field bed." Reproduced in mahogany, it demonstrates a neoclassic style noticeably lighter than its forebears. Thin posts terminate in urn finials.

Queen: Height 58½", with tester 77⅛"; Width 66⅜"; Length 87⅜". CW58-60

Double: Height 58½", with tester 77⅛"; Width 59⅛"; Length 81⅜". CW 58

Single: Height 58½", with tester 77⅛"; Width 44⅜"; Length 81⅜". CW58-S

CW58-S

BEDSTEAD

Possession of an elaborate bedstead was a measure of wealth in the eighteenth century. Beds were the most personalized of furnishings, sometimes custom-made by local cabinetmakers to fit the occupant's height. Most were fitted with wool hangings in winter to retain heat and ward off drafts, lighter cotton or mosquito netting in summer to keep out insects. This "pencil post" design was reproduced from an eighteenth-century New England antique, named in the twentieth century for the headposts that taper upward with slight beveling above the rails until they achieve a completely octagonal form. Like many beds of this period, there is a headboard but no footrail.

King: Height 79¾", with tester 80¾"; Width 74"-77"; Length 78"-81". 3344X

Queen: Height 79¾", with tester 80¾"; Width 57½"-60½"; Length 78"-81". 3334X

Double: Height 79¾", with tester 80¾"; Width 51"-54"; Length 73"-76". 3324X

Single: Height 79¾", with tester 80¾"; Width 36"-39"; Length 73"-76". 3314X

Martha Everard's field bedstead has crisp white cotton dimity curtains pulled up with a loop and button. This kind of folding bedstead was often used by military officers in encampment, hence the name field, or camp, bed.

3314X

CHEST

Reproduced from an original made in Taunton, Massachusetts, circa 1729, this handsome example of folk art features curving stems emerging from wavy lines bearing clusters of dots. Indications are that it was made by carpenter, drum maker, and gunsmith Robert Crossman (1702-1799).
Height: 20¼"; Width: 22⅝"; Depth: 12¾". 2314P

2314P

107

CW 11

TABLE

This small mahogany table was inspired by an English late baroque original circa 1760-1780. During this period, this table might have been used as a candle-stand, tea table, or, as might also be appropriate today, a small occasional table. Three gracefully refined cabriole legs terminate in snake feet.
Height 26¾"; Diameter 20¼". WF1210

SQUARE TEA TABLE

A delicate tripod base and finely carved pedestal distinguish this tilt-top table. Flowing lines indicate its rococo origins, yet also demonstrate the occasional preference for the "neat and plain" version of this sometimes highly ornamented style. Reproduced from an English original circa 1760, it would probably have served as a tea table for its original owners.
Height 26¾"; Top 25⅝" square. CW69

TEA TABLE

With the advent of the English tea trade with the Orient in the seventeenth century, a group of objects evolved that were related to the ritual of serving tea. This handsome tilt-top tea table is typical of those found in many homes for the specific purpose of serving tea, then stored away against the wall until the next occasion. The top also revolves for easier serving by means of a "bird cage" understructure. Reproduced from an antique made in Philadelphia circa 1775, it features ball-and-claw feet, cabriole legs, and a gracefully turned baluster.
Height 28¼"; Diameter 34¼". CW70

SMALL TEA TABLE

This simple reproduction tea table has versatile hidden features. The top revolves for easier serving via special "bird cage" construction connecting it to the base. The top also tilts up for compact storage against a wall. Made of mahogany, this table demonstrates an affection for the classical urn shape, evident in the base. Cabriole legs are lighter and more slender than those of the late baroque period. The original of this table was made in Massachusetts during the last quarter of the eighteenth century, just a few years after Bostonians dumped a shipload of British-imported tea into the harbor at the Boston Tea Party.
Height 27"; Diameter 21½". CW11

WF1210

CW69

CW70

WF1206

WF1233

CW27

WF1235

PEMBROKE TABLE

Inspired by a neoclassic antique made in Virginia circa 1790-1810, this table features tapered legs and delicate beading around the top. Originally intended as a breakfast table, this style allegedly was first made for the Countess of Pembroke in the 1720s.
Height 28"; Depth 29¾"; Width 39" open, 20¾" closed. WF1206

PEMBROKE TABLE

Reproduced from a Maryland or Virginia original circa 1790, this handsomely proportioned neoclassic table features white holly inlay, deep drawers, tapered legs, and a finely shaped oval top. In the eighteenth century, it would have been stored with the leaves down, then brought out into the room for tea or card playing.
Height 28¼"; Width 46¾" open, 22" closed. Depth 33". CW27

COFFEE TABLE

Although the coffee table is a modern innovation, this table is in the spirit of the eighteenth century and is offered to accommodate modern life-styles. Inspired by an antique New England couch frame circa 1730-1750, it features late baroque cabriole legs and finely turned stretchers.
Height 17¾"; Width 22½"; Length 46". WF1233

DROP-LEAF COFFEE TABLE

Coffee, tea, and chocolate offered an alternative to alcohol in the eighteenth century. While the coffee table was not developed until the twentieth century, this adaptation is based on a taller rococo American mahogany breakfast table circa 1760-1780 with cross stretchers, squared legs, and pierced side brackets.
Height 18¼"; Width 35" open, 20⅛" closed; Length 42". WF1235

CW 160

CW 2

DROP-LEAF TABLE

The original of this reproduction drop-leaf table was made in New York circa 1770. It features a clipped corner top, chamfered Marlborough legs, and openwork crossed stretchers. Tables of this form were often termed "breakfast tables," suggesting their original use.
Height 28½"; Depth 30¼"; Width 40¾" open, 20¼" closed. CW 160

CORNER TABLE

Designed to fit snugly into small spaces, this handsome reproduction mahogany drop-leaf corner table features refined, flowing cabriole legs on pad feet. The original was made in Massachusetts circa 1750-1780 and demonstrates the colonial penchant for wasting nothing, including space.
Height 26¾"; Diagonal width 35"; Depth 18" closed, 35" x 25" open. CW 2

Like dining and tea tables, card tables were made to fold for easy carrying. Here a footman prepares for a card party in the governor's parlor.

CW 156

CARD TABLE

Colonists whiled away their evenings entertaining their company with lavish dinners, good drink, and games of whist, quadrille, and loo around tables of various designs. In the South, particularly, hospitality was taken very seriously, to the point where some plantation owners were on the verge of being impoverished by the legions of friends and admirers who literally ate the owners out of house and home.

Fortunately, most plantation owners had long paid off the cost of such a handsome and, in the case of this half-round design, unusual late baroque English card table. This reproduction of a circa 1735 original features curvilinear scrolled knee brackets and exotic ball-and-claw feet. The half-round design enabled it to be folded and pushed against the wall when not in use.
Height 28¾"; Width 32¾"; Depth 32¼" open, 16⅛" closed.
CW 156

CW3

CARD TABLE

At the beginning of the sixteenth century, a positive mania for card games swept Europe. By the eighteenth century, it had reached epic proportions. Edmond Hoyle devised the rules for whist in 1760, setting off a new round of interest in card playing in England and America. Many an evening was spent over copious food, drink, and card playing in the parlor or dining room. Lord Botetourt, governor of Virginia, had a pair of card tables in the Palace parlor and twelve dozen packs of cards in a closet.

This card table, reproduced from a Newport, Rhode Island, original circa 1770, faithfully copies the chisel gouges, graceful cove molding, straight legs, and folding top of the original. As with tea tables and dining tables, card tables could be collapsed to facilitate storage against the wall when not in use.
Height 28¾"; Length 30¼"; Depth 15¾" closed, 31½" open. CW3

GAMING TABLE

Checkers, also known as "draughts," and backgammon, thought to be of Aztec origin, were popular during the eighteenth century. So was the ancient Persian game of chess, named after the shah who created it and played using rules developed in Spain by Ruy Lopez de Sigura in 1561. This mahogany Pembroke gaming table with identical front and back was reproduced from an English original circa 1800. Its gold tooled red and black leather backgammon board can be reversed to an inlaid maple and walnut checkerboard. The neoclassic penchant for decorating flat surfaces is apparent with rosewood banding and boxwood inlay on a mahogany field. The lower drawer opens from one side only.
Height 28¼"; Length 28"; Width 41½" open, 23" closed. CW84

CW84

CW318

CW8

CW141

CARD TABLE

Based on a Massachusetts original circa 1810, this reproduction card table aptly demonstrates neoclassic flat surface decoration. Elaborate top edging with satinwood and ebony inlays, ebony and holly inlays on legs and aprons, and crotch-grain mahogany apron banding are counterpoints to turned, reeded legs. Height 30⅜"; Width 37⅞"; Depth 17⅝" closed, 35¼" open. CW318

SPIDER TABLE

This six-legged table was used as a tea, breakfast, or writing table. Reproduced from an English example circa 1730, it has stretchers for extra support and pull-out slides used for holding cups when tea was drawn from large urns.
Height 28½"; Length 35¾"; Depth 12" closed, 24" open. CW141

TEA TABLE

Reproduced from a coastal Massachusetts antique circa 1750, this late baroque mahogany table offers graceful apron scalloping and delicate cabriole legs. Pine slides for holding teacups and mortise and tenon construction echo the construction of the original. Height 26¼"; Length 29¾"; Depth 18½". CW8

Thomas Chippendale illustrated china tables in his 1754 Gentleman and Cabinet-Maker's Director. *Status-conscious ladies displayed their porcelain tea services on such tables.*

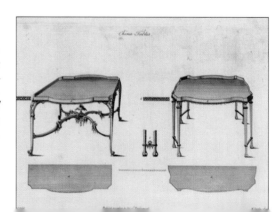

CW 192

BYRD CHINA TABLE

This extraordinary china table is reproduced from a Williamsburg, Virginia, original circa 1770. This antique has ties with the Byrd family of Virginia, and it is possible that the birds in the pierced rococo table skirt may be a reference to those featured in the Byrd coat of arms. The bird is the main decorative element in this table, one with carved anatomical features and the other in blind profile. The table's construction distinguishes it from English examples. Used to display tea china and silver or, alternatively, as a tea table, it was often left set up in the parlor even when not in use. The gallery was intended to prevent valuable objects from inadvertently being pushed off the edge.
Height 30 1/16"; Width 35 5/16"; Depth 23 3/16". CW 192

WF1258

WF1220

2615X

WF1259

TABLE

This single drawer, multi-purpose mahogany table is inspired by an English antique circa 1730. It features the turned legs, ball feet, and stretchers characteristic of the late baroque style.
Height 26⅜"; Width 24"; Depth 17". WF1258

DROP-LEAF TEA TABLE

This late baroque style table was inspired by a Massachusetts original circa 1740-1790. It was stored against the wall until needed for tea, dining, or card games. Its elegant proportions are enhanced by a scalloped skirt, notched corners, cabriole legs, and pad feet. One leg pivots to support the opened leaf.
Height 25¾"; Length 31"; Width 23½" open, 13½" closed. WF1220

TEA TABLE

Reproduced from a mid-eighteenth-century rural New England original, this handsome oval top table with pad feet served as a gathering point for enjoying card games, tea, and conversation in homes, taverns, and public buildings of the period.
Height 25¾"; Width 22¼"; Length 29¾". 2615X

DRESSING TABLE

Dressing tables were used by both men and women to hold personal effects such as pins, ribbons, and toiletries in its drawers, often with a dressing glass or wig stand on top. Inspired by a late baroque tidewater Virginia original circa 1730-1750, this delicately proportioned table features a graceful bead molding around the drawers.
Height 27½"; Width 28¾"; Depth 18¼". WF1259

TABLE

Decorative beading, a scalloped gallery with pierced handholds, and shaped panel doors distinguish this rococo bedside table. Reproduced from an English antique circa 1760, it originally held a chamberpot and was called a "night table."
Height 31"; Width 21"; Depth 19¼". CW57

CW57

TABLE

The simple design of this New England bedside table enhances its natural beauty: solid curly maple as the primary wood with bird's-eye maple and veneer banding. Reproduced from a late eighteenth-century single drawer nightstand, this very popular type of table was used also as a chair-side stand, sewing table, or work table. A tiger maple and cherry adaptation also is available.
Height 27½"; Width 18¾"; Depth 17¾". 2614T

2614T

117

WF1214

TABLE

Inspired by a circa 1790 English antique, this mahogany table serves many purposes. As in the eighteenth century, it can be used as a writing, dressing, or occasional table in a dressing room, living room, or study. The neoclassic style antique inspiring this copy featured tapered legs and a stamped oval brass. The Marlborough legs and cast brass substituted in this interpretation suggest the rococo style of 1750-1775. Height 28″; Width 28¾″; Depth 16″. WF1214

WF3204

DRESSING TABLE

This dressing table was inspired by the "neat and plain" version of rococo styling exemplified by a tidewater Virginia original circa 1760-1780. Fascination for the exotic is evident in the pierced fretwork brackets derived from Oriental inspired designs made in England and America during the flourishing East Indies tea trade. The straight, clean line of the legs also is inspired from Chinese design. Nine inches longer than the original, this piece is suitable as a desk, writing table, side table, or serving table.
Height 29½″; Width 42″; Depth 21″. WF3204

WF1038

CW37

Hanging Shelf

Originally designed for storing books, this hanging wall shelf is perfect for display of porcelain, pewter, and other precious objects today. This interpretation of a late eighteenth-century English shelf features open fretwork of provincial rococo style. The bottom drawer is a handy storage place for smaller valuables. Height 34″; Width 24″; Depth 7″. WF1038

Hanging Shelf

Thirteenth-century Gothic tracery and eighteenth-century Oriental piercing are both significant features of the rococo style. The delicate open fretwork in this reproduction of an English circa 1765 shelf exemplifies how both of these influences converged. Height 39″; Width 36″; Depth 7″. CW37

Hanging Cupboard

This utilitarian hanging wall cupboard is adapted from a Pennsylvania antique circa 1720-1760. It probably was used in a kitchen or pantry and features a small hinged door with molded edge and fielded panel, opening to a single shelf. The drawer's molded edge is complemented by a center knob pull. A broad cove cornice decorates the top.
Height 24⅜″; Width 21⅛″; Depth 10¹¹⁄₁₆″. 2714C

2714C

Fire screens kept the scorching heat and smoke of a roaring fire away from the faces of our ancestors while still allowing heat to warm their bodies. Peyton Randolph, speaker of the Virginia House of Burgesses and first president of the Continental Congress, kept a pair of expensive fire screens in his parlor.

CW 149

CW 92

CW 182

KETTLE STAND

With the Western passion for tea came unique pieces of furniture such as this kettle stand, reproduced from an English original circa 1725-1730. It features the cabriole legs and turned post typical of late baroque design. The copper top is impervious to heat damage, making it a perfect resting place for a tea kettle.
Height 21″; Diameter 10″.
CW149

FIRESCREEN

Firescreens were used to shield a sitter's face from exposure to the heat of an open fireplace. This handsome rococo mahogany firescreen is reproduced from an original made in England, circa 1760. Height 47½″; Panel 17¾″ square. CW92

KETTLE STAND

Despite stiff duties on imported tea, many colonists enjoyed nothing more than a cup of tea by the fire on a chilly winter afternoon. This reproduction of an English antique circa 1750 held a cup, saucer, and tea urn with ease.
Height 22¾″; Top — large 12″, small 4⅞″ diameter. CW182

CANDLESTAND

In the days before electricity, candlestands such as this were made in a range of heights, often in pairs. This handsome reproduction of an English original circa 1740 features an octagonal tray with gallery, subtly turned pedestal, and a tripod base with cabriole legs.
Height 38½″; Top 10½″ square.
CW49

BASIN STAND

Made in England circa 1740, the original of this late baroque mahogany reproduction was used for bathing in the bedroom. It held a round ceramic or metal washbowl on top, soap and powder in the drawers, and a bottle of water on the bottom shelf. The drawer unit is made of twelve delicately dovetailed pieces. Cabriole legs are dovetailed into the bottom shelf.
Height 32″; Diameter 11¾″.
CW5

CW49

CW5

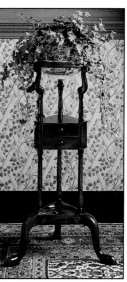

CW5

WF 1164

DESK AND BOOKCASE

This desk and bookcase was inspired by a rococo antique made by a rural tidewater Virginia cabinetmaker circa 1765-1785. During this time, radical Virginians began pushing for greater autonomy and freedom from British rule. Moderate Virginians sided with the crown. Jefferson and Washington formulated ideas that eventually took them from the House of Burgesses to the Continental Congress. Correspondence of all kinds may have been conceived, written, and read while seated at a tall, paneled, bracket-footed desk such as this. Three adjustable shelves hold books. Seven pigeonholes separate important papers. The drawers originally held sealing wax, writing paper, ink, and sand to dry freshly penned documents.

Desk and Bookcase: Height 81½"; Width 40½"; Depth 21¾". WF 1164

Desk: Height 41"; Width 39⅝"; Depth 21¾". WF 1165

DESK AND BOOKCASE

In the late 1770s, Williamsburg was a relatively small but urbane community with a respected college. During this "Age of Enlightenment," gentlemen of Virginia and professors of the college gathered together to exchange ideas on philosophy, literature, and new understanding of the natural world. A prized possession of an educated man of means was his desk and bookcase, housing important books, documents, and records. This reproduction of a Massachusetts antique circa 1770 is made of solid mahogany. It features bold brasses, shaped door panels, and a stylized shell carved on the gently scalloped apron, all features of New England rococo design. The slant top drops down to create a writing surface and to reveal a wealth of pockets and drawers for storing important papers and writing objects. The doors, drawer, and slant top all have locks, an important feature for household security in the eighteenth century.

Desk and Bookcase: Height 61″; Width 41½″; Depth 20½″. CW1

Desk only: Height 40″; Width 41½″; Depth 20½″. CW1½

CW1

CW 168-68

BOOKCASE

In 1760, Oliver Gold-smith wrote *Citizen of the World,* people were talking about Voltaire's *Candide,* and Jean Jacques Rousseau was finishing work on *Julie, or La Nouvelle Héloïse.* Some of these works may well have found their way into the original English bookcase circa 1760. The simple, graceful proportions and unpretentious brasses of this reproduction allow the handsome grain of the mahogany to stand out. Gathered curtains usually hung behind glazed doors to protect valuable books from damage by sunlight. Height 79½"; Width 46¾"; Depth 15¾". CW 164

LIBRARY TABLE

Lord Botetourt, who served as the royal governor of Virginia between 1768 and 1770, kept a "mahogany library table containing papers public and private" in his dining room at the Governor's Palace in Williamsburg. This multi-purpose room served as his office between meals. Identical on both sides, this reproduction of a massive but simply styled circa 1765 English rococo library table, often referred to as a "partner's desk" today, has nine locking drawers, handsome brass pulls and escutcheons, and a bold mahogany grain pattern. It is available in two lengths with a modesty panel and file drawer optional.
Height 31"; Length 58¾"; Width 40¼". CW 168
Height 31"; Length 68¾"; Width 40¼". CW 168-68

Between meals Lord Botetourt used his dining room as an office. His mahogany library table, which in 1770 contained "papers public and private," is set out with a portfolio, inkstand, taper jack, and snuffer stand.

CLOCKS
IN THE EIGHTEENTH CENTURY

When the first settlers landed in Virginia, even the best of clocks were imprecise timekeepers. Over the next 150 years, European clockmakers improved their products with innovations such as the use of the pendulum and a host of mechanical refinements. By the mid-eighteenth century, good quality clocks kept time to within a few seconds a day.

In England, a dozen or more trades made parts for clock movements, and cabinetmakers or even specialist clock case makers fabricated cases. Some American clockmakers built their own mechanisms, but many imported movements from England, installing them in locally made cases. The clockmaker whose name appeared on the dial was often as much an assembler, finisher, and repairer as a fabricator.

Tall case clocks were the most common type. Their design reflected their mechanism: the movement sitting at the top of the case and the pendulum and driving weights suspended below. They were imposing pieces of furniture with their faces and cases fashioned to current tastes in design and decoration. Such clocks were expensive, frequently costing as much as an elaborate bed with all its hangings or a major piece of case furniture. Only middling and upper-class Virginians could afford such a luxury, which they displayed with pride in their best rooms.

— JAMES M. GAYNOR

James M. Gaynor, *curator of mechanical arts, has done extensive research on woodworking tools and on the material world of slavery in eighteenth-century Virginia. He is preparing an exhibit on documented tools for the DeWitt Wallace Decorative Arts Gallery.*

THE LORD DUNMORE TALL CASE CLOCK

When the Virginia colony formed a volunteer militia in 1775, Lord Dunmore, the royal governor, became alarmed and seized the colony's store of gunpowder in Williamsburg. He fled during the ensuing uprising, leaving all his possessions behind including a Scottish rococo clock circa 1765. Copied from Dunmore's original, this reproduction features a removable hood that slides forward to expose an eight-day hourly bell strike typical of fine clocks of this period. The face has a silvered brass chapter ring, corner spandrels, scalloped edges around an inset seconds dial, and exquisitely cut hands.
Height 94½"; Width 20⅛"; Depth 10½". CW730

CW736

THE LYNCHBURG TALL CASE CLOCK

Made in America in the early nineteenth century, this mahogany tall case clock is delicate in scale and detail. A hand-painted face features colored spandrels, gold decoration, and a calendar wheel. An intricate moon dial has global maps, moon phases, and ship and cottage scenes. While the clock's original face bears the inscription of "Williams & Victor/Lynchburg," it appears that this Virginia clockmaking and silversmithing firm actually imported the case from New England. The movement may have come from New England, have been imported from England, or have been made in their own Lynchburg shop.
Height 96⅞"; Width 20⅞"; Depth 10¼". CW736

CW733

THE BUCKS COUNTY TALL CASE CLOCK

This design was popular in England for decades before making its way to the colonies. This laggardly pace may have been because some clockmakers' shops often were located in small, very conservative rural communities. A reproduction of an original Pennsylvania clock circa 1750-1760 signed by J. Dyer of Bucks County, this clock illustrates backcountry cabinetwork. The case is augmented by a fine eight-day hourly strike bell and solid brass face with silvered chapter ring. The original movement was made by Augustine Neisser of Germantown, Pennsylvania.
Height 86¼"; Width 20¼"; Depth 11¼". CW733

EIGHTEENTH — CENTURY
LOOKING GLASSES

Mirrors, called looking glasses in the eighteenth century, were not utilized solely for reflecting one's own image. Before the advent of electric light, looking glasses offered other practical uses as well. On a cloudy day or a winter afternoon, a large looking glass placed opposite a window could brighten a room considerably by reflecting back the daylight. At times, looking glasses were also used to multiply the effect of candlelight at night.

— RONALD L. HURST
Curator of Furniture

CWLG6

NEOCLASSIC OVAL LOOKING GLASS

Based on an English antique of about 1790, this intricately detailed piece demonstrates the interest in classical motifs by the urn finial and the lightly scaled gilt wood frame. The oval form was highly fashionable in the late eighteenth and early nineteenth centuries. The reproduction is available in gold leaf with an adaptation in gold metal leaf.
Glass 15½" x 25½"; Overall size 22" x 49½".
CWLG3

SHELL AND EAGLES LOOKING GLASS

Made in England circa 1725, this mirror features a rich gilt gesso frame. The carved shell and symmetrically placed eagle heads at the top are typical of late baroque design influences. This reproduction is made using gold leaf and plain glass. An adaptation features gold metal leaf and/or beveled glass.
Glass 16½" x 28½"; Overall size 22¼" x 41".
CWLG6

PARCEL GILT LOOKING GLASS

Made of walnut and gilt gesso, this English mirror of about 1740 features the tight scrolls, floral volutes, and acanthus leaves typical of late baroque. Wealthy plantation owners often owned pairs of looking glasses much like this. The reproduction is in gold leaf. An adaptation features gold metal leaf and/or beveled glass.
Glass 22" x 34"; Overall size 28½" x 58". CWLG15

CWLG15

CWLG5

Inventories reveal that many Virginia gentry women, among them Betty Randolph, primped at looking glasses and dressing tables in their bedchambers. The tables were frequently draped with a skirted cover called a "toilet" sometimes corrupted in the local vernacular to "twilight."

RANDOLPH LOOKING GLASS

Serpentine curves and symmetry are reflected in this reproduction Randolph wall mirror. The original is a late baroque gilt mirror with plain glass made in England circa 1720-1750. It also is available in a variety of adaptations, including walnut, gold metal leaf, beveled glass, and an easel version. Glass 15″ × 21¼″. Overall size 15¾″ × 22″. CWLG10

PRINCE OF WALES LOOKING GLASS

Mirrors were often hung high on a wall or between two windows to reflect as much light as possible into dark corners. Gilt Prince of Wales feathers adorn this delicately carved, handsomely grained burl walnut frame. The reproduction is based on an original featuring ornate late baroque symmetry. It was made in England circa 1740-1750.
Glass 20¼″ x 27¼″; Overall size 28¾″ x 46½″. CWLG5

WYTHE LOOKING GLASS

The original Wythe looking glass was made about 1725. This reproduction features simple, sophisticated proportions in its beveled glass and black frame. Adaptations are available in several frame finishes as well as an easel version. Glass 13¼″ × 23¼″; Overall size 14¾″ × 24¾″. CWLG11

CWLG10   CWLG11

CWLG8

CWLG9

WA 1032

ROCOCO SHELL LOOKING GLASS

Stylized gilt shells, a gilt border, skillfully carved mahogany curves, and symmetrical design blend late baroque and rococo influences. The original of this English mirror was made about 1760. Also comes with plain glass. Glass 15½" × 27¼"; Overall size 22" × 42¼". CWLG8

TAYLOE LOOKING GLASS

The pleasing, simple lines of this reproduction are duplicated from those of a late baroque antique made in England about 1720. Like the original, it features rich mahogany, 24kt gold leaf, and a beveled glass. Adaptations are available in other variations. Glass 21¼" x 29½"; Overall size 23½" x 31½". WA1028

WA1028

PHILADELPHIA LOOKING GLASS

A label on the back of the original of this mahogany rococo mirror suggests that it was sold, and possibly made, by John Elliott about 1755. He emigrated from England to Philadelphia to open an import business and to take advantage of the changing plate glass technology that made it possible to meet the booming demand for domestically framed looking glasses in the colonies. Also comes with plain glass. Glass 12½" x 21¾"; Overall size 18¾" x 35¼". CWLG9

JOHN ELLIOTT LOOKING GLASS

This circa 1755 mirror is labeled from the Philadelphia shop of John Elliott, an English émigré who imported mirrors and also manufactured them. The original may be American or British. The reproduction uses plain glass, with a beveled glass adaptation. Glass 15½" x 27¼"; Overall size 21½" x 40¾". WA1032

WA1067

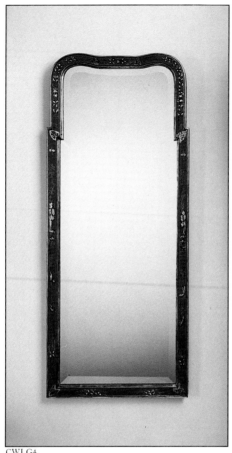

CWLG4

CWLG2

CWLG14

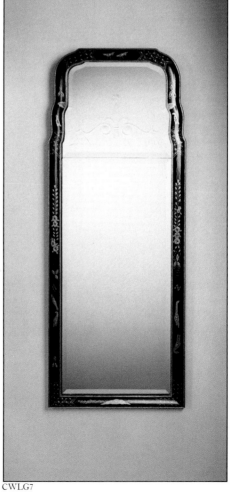

CWLG7

LIGHTFOOT LOOKING GLASS

Pierced gilt, elaborate scrolls, ruffles, foliage, and fruit swags typify this English rococo design, circa 1740-1760. The reproduction is gold leaf with plain glass, adapted using gold metal leaf and/or beveled glass.
Glass 20" x 28¾"; Overall size 26½" x 46". WA1067

ENGLISH JAPANNED LOOKING GLASS

English gilded birds and plants adorn a lacquered frame in this late baroque original, circa 1715. The reproduction, in black, has two pieces of plain glass. Adaptations have one panel of beveled glass and/or other frame colors.
Glass 14½" x 39½"; Overall size 18" x 43". CWLG4

GIRANDOLE LOOKING GLASS

An American eagle, circa 1800-1820, surveys the view from above convex glass framed by gilt gesso and curved candle arms. The reproduction features gold leaf, adapted in gold metal leaf.
Glass diameter 11¾"; Overall size 17½" x 39"; Depth 7". CWLG2

AMERICAN JAPANNED LOOKING GLASS

Inspired by items brought back from the Far East, this late baroque mirror of New York origin, circa 1730-1740, features gilding, painting, and lacquering, a technique called japanning. The reproduction is black with plain glass, adapted with other lacquered colors, and/or beveled glass.
Glass 34⅜" x 15⅜"; Overall size 44" x 18¼". CWLG14

CHINESE BIRDS LOOKING GLASS

The reproduction of an English late baroque original, circa 1710-1720, features gilded Oriental motifs on a black lacquered frame. The beveled mirror is made in two parts. Adaptations use other variations, including other colors and/or an engraved top.
Glass 15" x 44¼"; Overall size 18¾" x 48". CWLG7

CWLG16

PEDIMENTED LOOKING GLASS

This mirror is reproduced from a late baroque English original of gold leaf and beveled glass, circa 1725-1740, that was originally purchased by a New England household. Much skill was required to make looking glass frames. The plate glass was expensive to manufacture and broke easily. As a consequence, domestically produced looking glasses were rare, and the high cost of shipping made imported looking glasses even more precious. This mirror is also adapted in gold metal leaf.
Glass 18" × 30"; Overall size 51¾" × 24¾". CWLG16

TEXTILES

IN THE EIGHTEENTH CENTURY

American colonists were removed from the European centers by an ocean, but that did not prevent them from following fashion trends. Worldwide trade meant that a colonist could own a carpet from Turkey, damask from China, linen from Europe, and printed cottons from India or England. Although some Americans did make their own textiles, home production was never able to match the quality or quantity of imported goods.

Clothing textiles changed frequently in response to fashion's dictates, but the long-term nature of household textiles meant that they were conservative, with new patterns evolving more slowly than for clothing. Textiles took up a greater proportion of the average person's budget than they do today. Aware of the cost and fragility of textiles, many people protected their expensive upholstery from sun and dust by using slipcovers of less expensive materials such as washable linen checks and stripes. Today considered casual, checks were used in the most elegant homes as well as in modest ones and taverns. (See page 137)

If checked and striped linens were among the least expensive furnishing fabrics, silks were the most costly. Only the wealthiest colonists used silk for bed hangings or chair upholstery. More common—and considerably more serviceable—were fine wool worsteds, often woven to imitate silks. The best cottons were made in India for the export market. India chintzes were prized for their lively designs, bright colorfast hues, and polished surfaces. Today's use of the term "chintz" for polished cotton comes from the Indian practice of glazing chintzes with rice starch.

The diplomatic Lord Botetourt purchased coronation portraits of King George III and Queen Charlotte for his official residence in Virginia. Court painter Allan Ramsay's studio provided many such state portraits for aristocratic or ambassadorial houses.

Europeans competed with Indian imports by printing with wood blocks rather than using the labor-intensive hand painting method used by the Indians. In the second half of the eighteenth century, both English and Indian printed cottons were increasingly available. Eventually both came to be called "chintzes." Around 1750 the technology to print colorfast textiles with engraved copperplates was developed, producing monochromatic designs with delicate details. They quickly reached America. In 1758, Benjamin Franklin sent fifty-six yards of copperplate-printed cotton from London to his wife in Philadelphia to furnish an entire room. This instance underscores the fashion for having all of the textiles in a room match, or be "en suite." Today these textiles are often called *toiles de Jouy* (French for fabrics of Jouy, France, where many copperplate textiles were made.) However, most of the copperplate-printed textiles imported into the colonies were of English manufacture and were known as "copperplate calicoes," not "toiles."

Eighteenth-century textiles differ in some ways from their modern counterparts. Only natural fibers were available. Those most often used were wool, silk, cotton, and linen. Although some wide textiles were made, most silks were narrow, as little as nineteen to twenty-two inches wide; today's reproductions are often woven double wide to accommodate the modern looms and avoid waste. One thing has not changed — textiles added warmth and color to yesterday's interiors as they do today.

— LINDA R. BAUMGARTEN

Linda R. Baumgarten, *curator of textiles*, wrote Eighteenth-Century Clothing at Williamsburg. *She has also written several articles on period costume and on slave clothing.*

BED HANGINGS
IN THE EIGHTEENTH CENTURY

A tall-post bed hung with yards of expensive textiles was considered as much a status symbol during the colonial period as an expensive car is to some people today. During the seventeenth century, some householders put their best bed in the parlor where it could readily be seen by visitors; and even when beds were removed to bedchambers in the eighteenth century they still represented a major investment of funds. Very little of this investment was in the wooden framework, but rather in the mattresses and bolsters stuffed with curled horsehair, feather beds and pillows, and a surround of hangings requiring from twenty-five to seventy yards of fabric and sometimes more, depending on the style of the bed. (fig. 1) The records of upholsterer Thomas Chippendale reveal that the beds he supplied his English customers required from 27½ yards of "morine" (worsted) for a field bed up to 64¾ yards of cotton for a large dome bed.[1]

"Bed furniture," as the textile components were often called, consisted of numerous pieces. The most elegant beds were topped with a carved wooden or papier-mâché

FIG. 1

cornice which might be painted, gilded, covered with colored paper, or covered with fabric matching the curtains, carefully shaped and glued to the wood. (fig. 2) Many American beds came with cornices, as well. George Washington's beech bedstead and window curtains ordered in 1759 were each to have a "neat cut Cornish" covered with the blue plate-printed cotton of the bed and window curtains.[2] Upholsterers frequently advertised that they could supply bed and window cornices for their customers.

Running around the top of the bed below the cornice were the three fabric valances, shaped and trimmed in various ways depending on the style of the bed. (fig. 3) Better beds had an additional set of

FIG. 3

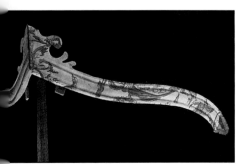

FIG. 2

1. Christopher Gilbert, *The Life and Work of Thomas Chippendale*, Volume I, p. 147 and 228.
2. Helen Maggs Fede, *Washington Furniture at Mount Vernon*, p. 18.

136

three or four inner valances hanging inside the bed to camouflage the rings and other hardware from the occupant's view. Usually made of cloth stretched over a frame, the tester was the ceiling of the bed. The headcloth hung down from the back of the bed and covered the headboard unless the headboard was particularly decorative. The curtains hung down to the floor, usually enclosing the bed entirely and giving warmth and privacy to the occupants. Beds had from four to six curtains, depending on whether the foot curtains were split at the footposts (giving the bed six curtains in all) or whether they were made double wide to curve around each post (giving the bed a total of four curtains). The spaces between the mattress and the floor usually had another set of deeper valances called base valances or "bases." These corresponded to modern "dust

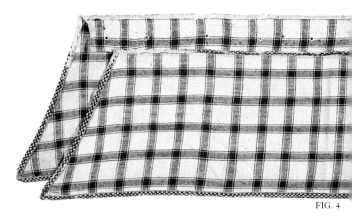

FIG. 4

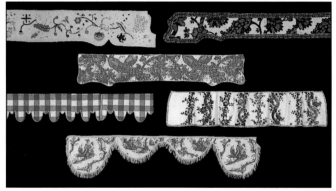

FIG. 5

ruffles." The top covering of the mattress consisted of a counterpane of matching fabric, a quilt, or a woven coverlet (the word "bedspread" was not generally used during the period).

FIG. 6

The valances and bases were sometimes nailed directly to the wooden parts of the bed frame. A pattern of nail holes on antique bedsteads today provides us important clues about how the beds were originally furnished. In other instances, valances and bases were held up with studs or nail heads that slipped through thread eyelets worked into the valances; valances treated this way were easily removed for cleaning. (fig. 4)

Not everyone had expensive tall-post beds, of course. Low-post beds without curtains were used by many people, especially those without funds for elaborate curtains.

Bed hangings were made in a variety of styles. (fig. 5) Valances and bases might consist of a flat, continuous piece running around the bed; they could also be gathered, cut and shaped, or draped in elaborate festoons. Bed curtains were often simple, flat panels with rings at the top to slide on the rods fitted to the bedstead. The rings were either stitched directly to the curtain or looped through narrow tapes sewn at intervals along the top of the curtain. (fig. 6) The latter treatment allowed the rings to be easily removed for laundering the curtains, without unstitching each time. (The "tab curtains" of today seem to have been inspired by such curtains which have lost their original rings.) Curtains were made wide enough to enclose the bed entirely and were often left unlined; sometimes the edges were bound with tape, but occasionally the selvages were the only edge finish. Hems at the top and bottom were narrow so as not to waste the fabric.

More elaborate beds were made with curtains that drew up in "drapery style." (fig. 7) These required a bedstead with pulleys at the top through which cords (called "lines") ran. The cords ran through small rings —sometimes called

FIG. 7

FIG. 8 (detail)

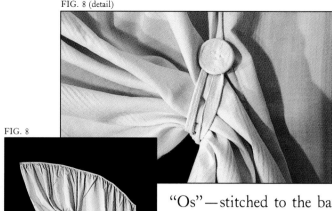

FIG. 8

his *Cabinet Dictionary* said that camp beds were used not only for encampments but also for "domestic use, and suit low rooms, either for servants or children to sleep on." Hangings for these beds consisted of "throw-over furniture" — curtains and tester (or roof) sewn together in one piece, intended to be dropped down over the wooden framework quickly and easily. The curtains were fastened up with loops and buttons or were tied back to the bed posts. These functional folding beds did not have valances, though the fancier stationary field beds that were not portable sometimes had cornices and similar elaborate trimmings.

Late in the eighteenth century the use of working drapery curtains gradually went out of style, at which time many beds lost their original pulleys and cloak pins, which were discarded when styles changed. Draped effects were not abandoned, however; increasingly elaborate stationary drapery was used in place of valances at the top of the bed. (fig. 9) At the same time, a new style was coming in: there was a movement among some away from the use of curtains to enclose the bed fully. Some beds were designed with no foot curtains for the sake of fresh air, which was now recognized to be more healthy than the stuffy air inside a curtained bed.

— LINDA R. BAUMGARTEN
Curator of Textiles

"Os"—stitched to the back of each curtain in a curving path; the cords proceeded up over the pulleys and back down for access. When the cords were pulled, the curtains were drawn up in single or double swags, the latter called "double drapery." (fig. 1) Drapery beds required cloak pins or knobs on the posts on which to tie off the cords when the curtains were drawn up; these pins have usually been removed on antique bedsteads, but still show up as holes in the bedposts—clear evidence that the bed was once hung in drapery style. Thomas Chippendale designed and made many beds in the drapery style; his *Gentleman and Cabinet-maker's Director* illustrates many such beds and shows the placement of the pulleys to accomplish the end result. Americans, too, followed this style, as evidenced in upholsterers' advertisements and in surviving bedsteads with pulley laths and holes for cloak pins on their posts.

A simpler way to achieve a draped effect is to raise the curtains with buttons and loops sewn to the curtains themselves. (fig. 8) In this treatment, a button is positioned at the front of the curtain and a corresponding loop is stitched directly behind on the back of the curtain; the material is gathered up and held in place by bringing the loop up over the button. Hepplewhite gives both options in plate 96 of his 1787 *Cabinet-maker and Upholsterer's Guide*. He shows a bed with gathered valances and bases; the curtain is shown in single drapery which "is drawn up and fastened by lines [cords] at the head, or with loop and button."

Tent or camp beds were designed with testers that curved up in an arch or angled upward in a tent shape. True tent beds had tester laths that folded for portability and ease of storage. Thomas Sheraton in

FIG. 9

WINDOW CURTAINS
IN THE EIGHTEENTH CENTURY

Today's rooms do not seem complete without window curtains, so it may be difficult for twentieth-century people to understand the scarcity of window curtains in the eighteenth century. Many rooms even in the homes of the wealthy went uncurtained until the very late eighteenth century when curtains came into more general use. Those who did have window curtains used them more often in bedchambers "en suite" with the bed curtains to give an elegant effect and ensure greater privacy. In spite of their expense, window curtains were used by some people but never in the quantities we use them today. To protect their investment, many people removed the curtains during the summer or when they were away from home for extended periods.

In the absence of window curtains, people used other options. The louvered exterior window shutters on some homes were not just decorative; they were an excellent way to block the hot rays of the sun while still letting in breezes during the summer months. The interior shutters on some windows could be folded across the windows at night for privacy or to keep in the heat of a warm fire. Fabric blinds similar to modern window shades were called "spring blinds" or "spring curtains." They were made

of brown linen or green worsted and were fixed to a roller with a spring mechanism that allowed them to be raised or lowered. (fig. 1)

FIG. 1

FIG. 2

Venetian blinds, made of painted or stained wooden slats, were also available, although they were relatively expensive. Advertising in Philadelphia in 1767 John Webster extolled the virtues of Venetian blinds: "The newest invented Venetian sun blinds for windows, on the best principles, stain'd to any colour, moves to any position, so as to give different lights, screens from the scorching rays of the sun, draws up as a curtain, and prevents from being overlooked [i.e. gives privacy], and is the greatest preserver of furniture of any thing ever invented."[1] In his 1803 *Cabinet Dictionary*, Thomas Sheraton described Venetian blinds that "draw up by pullies fixed in a lath 1 inch thick, the same as a festoon window curtain."

Both Webster and Sheraton compared Venetian blinds to window curtains. They referred to the "festoon" or Venetian curtain that drew straight up by a series of cords and pulleys in the same manner as the Venetian blind. In use throughout the eighteenth century, this curtain was a flat panel when lowered, but draped in puffs or festoons

1. *Pennsylvania Journal*, August 20, 1767.

when pulled to the top of the window by the cord at the side. (fig. 2) A series of cords ran along the back of the curtain through small rings sewn in vertical rows, up over the pulleys fixed into a wooden lath at the top, where they were tied together and fastened to a single cord that ran down the side. Two cloak pins were spaced six to eight inches apart at the side so the cord could be tied off to hold the curtain up at any level. Thomas Chippendale weighted some of his draw-up curtains with lead "plummets" at the bottom so they would hang more evenly and lower more easily.

Another type of draw-up curtain was the drapery curtain (fig. 3), made like the drapery bed cur-

FIG. 3

tain discussed in the section on bed hangings. In this design, the rings and cords traveled in a curved, diagonal path up the back of each curtain panel over the pulley fixed in each top corner. Different drapery effects were achieved depending on the path the cords took and whether the panels were gathered or flat. This curtain required two cloak pins on each side since the panels drew up independently and were tied off on each side.

By the 1780s a type of curtain similar to modern draw draperies came into use. (fig. 4) Called "French Rod" curtains, they drew aside by pulleys, but unlike similar curtain panels earlier in the century, the rods overlapped slightly in the

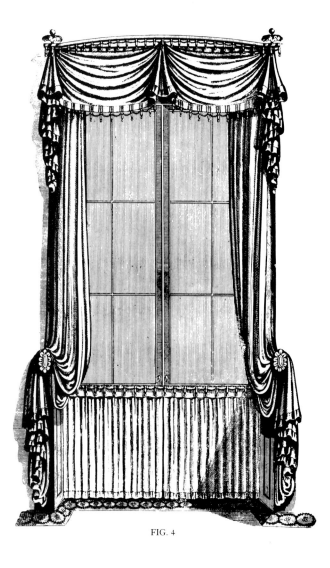

FIG. 4

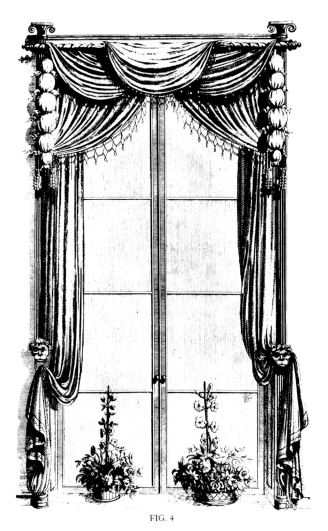

FIG. 4

center, completely closing any gaps when the curtains were closed. These curtains were usually finished with elaborate valances or draped effects at the top.

Throughout the period, simple straight panel curtains were used in a variety of ways. (fig. 5) Used singly or in pairs, they were shirred on rods, nailed to the top of the window frame, or hung from rings on a rod. In functional interiors like taverns, they were shirred on a rod over the lower half of the window like a modern "cafe" curtain.

Valances of various shapes were sometimes used with straight panels as with French rod cur-

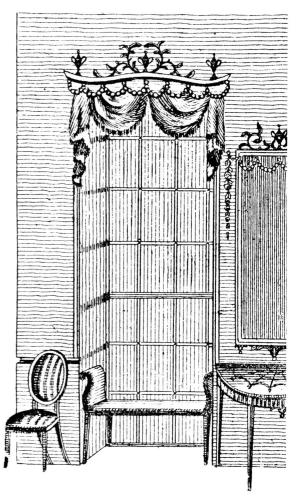

FIG. 6

DECEMBER.   DECEMBRE.

FIG. 5

tains. When the curtains were used in a bedchamber, the valances corresponded with the shape of the bed valances.

By the late eighteenth century, fixed drapery came into fashion. (fig. 6) No longer functional, like the earlier drapery curtains had been, these consisted of combinations of swags and drapery and were fixed in place at the top of the window. They were sometimes used along with curtains at the sides and sometimes used alone. In spite of this apparent elaboration, fixed drapery curtains were often cut very simply and economically to save fabric. A swag could be made from a simple trapezoid or from a rectangular piece of fabric gathered on diagonal lines. Using a series of straight and diagonal lines on "railroaded" fabric (cut lengthwise with the selvages), a set of curtains could be cut out and

constructed without wasting an inch of the precious textile. (fig. 7)

Not all window curtains were lined, expecially those made of sturdy worsteds like moreen. When linings were used, popular choices were a thin silk "lutestring" or calico. Flannel innerlinings were not used in the eighteenth century.

As with bed curtains, window curtains were often topped by papier-mâché or wooden cornices, painted, gilded, or covered with the fabric.

— Linda R. Baumgarten
Curator of Textiles

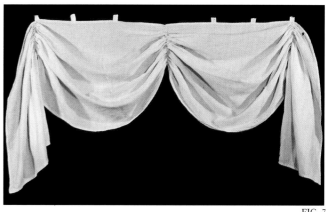

FIG. 7

PANELS WITH VALANCES AND FRENCH ROD CURTAINS

Panel curtains range from a single flat curtain shirred on a rod or nailed directly into the woodwork to elaborate constructions of the late eighteenth century on a French rod and topped with shaped or draped valances. The panels may fall to the sill or to the floor; half curtains (similar to today's "cafe curtains") gathered on a rod or heavy cord are appropriate in informal settings. Curtains using one or two panels occur throughout the eighteenth century. Their style depended on the type of textile chosen and the shape of the valance, if used. Up to 1750 or 1760 valances had robustly curved shapes and "ear" projections at the sides. Sometimes they were trimmed with tape applied in scrolls. After midcentury, valances, whether shaped in scallops, flattened curved scrolls, or gathered, gradually became lighter. Late in the century valances often took the form of stationary drapery.

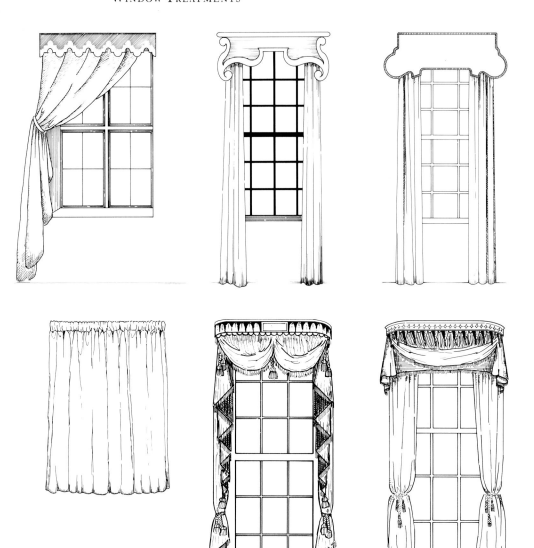

DRAW-UP DRAPERY CURTAINS

Draw-up drapery curtains are made of two panels, each of which has a cord traveling in a curved diagonal path up to the outer corners where it runs over a pulley and back down to the side. When the curtains are pulled up to the top, they create swags and tails. There are no fixed rules dictating the path of the cords and rings on the back of the curtain; this is arrived at through experimentation and depends on the weight of the fabric and the final effect desired. An asymmetrical effect is achieved by using a single panel drawn up to one side. Drapery curtains are usually provided with cornices at the top to hide the pulleys. The curtains were most popular from about 1750 to 1780 and are typical of rococo design.

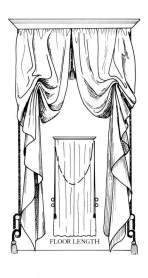

FLOOR LENGTH

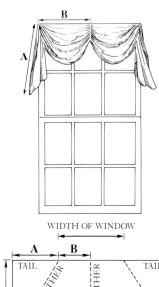

WIDTH OF WINDOW

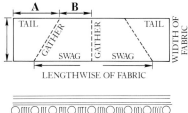

LENGTHWISE OF FABRIC

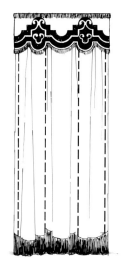

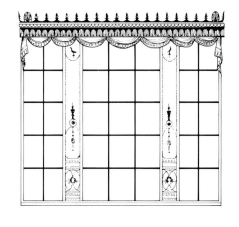

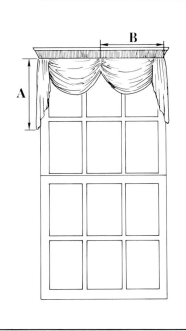

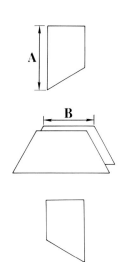

FIXED DRAPERY CURTAINS

Fixed drapery curtains are made from cut and sewn shapes and panels to create the effect of swags and tails. The pieces are fixed to the window and do not move like draw-up drapery curtains. There are many variations of the style, but most eighteenth-century examples were cut to conserve fabric by using straight-edged shapes, not curved, and by using the full selvage width of the fabric, cutting the pieces like a puzzle wherever possible. There are no fixed rules about proportion; this must be judged by eye depending on the size of the window and the weight of the fabric. The proportions gradually got heavier later in the period. Fixed drapery curtains were used from about 1775 to the early nineteenth century and are especially attractive in neoclassical interiors.

DASHES REPRESENT PATH OF RINGS ON BACK

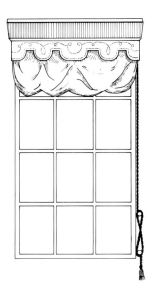

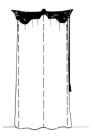

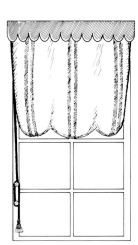

DRAW-UP FESTOON OR VENETIAN CURTAINS

Draw-up festoon curtains pull straight up by means of cords and pulleys. The curtains form puffs at the top of the window when fully drawn up. They may be used with wooden cornices, fabric valances, or both. The curtain panel may be flat or slightly gathered, and its length may extend to the sill or down to the floor depending on the effect desired. The width of the window will dictate how many cords are needed to achieve the desired number of puffs. This type of curtain was used throughout the eighteenth century but was considered slightly old-fashioned by 1800.

Lord Botetourt used expensive crimson damask for curtains and upholstery in the ceremonial upper chamber at the Palace where he met with his Council and visiting dignitaries.

33105   SALMON

33101   GOLD

33100   OLIVE GREEN

33102   CRIMSON

33106   RESEDA

CW 174 SOFA, page 58.

Bruton Damask

This handsome silk and cotton woven fabric is adapted from a bright gold antique silk damask made in France or England from 1790 to 1810. It is 52″ wide with a 21¼″ vertical repeat.

CAROLINA TOILE

The modern designation "toile" refers to copperplate-printed textiles of French origin. Carolina Toile is a 100 percent cotton fabric reproduced from an eighteenth-century English copperplate-printed cotton and linen counterpane. It is 54″ wide with a 36″ vertical repeat.

78833   COLONIAL GREEN

78830   RED*

78832   INDIGO

78831   HENNA

COLONIAL DRESS BROCADE

This cotton and rayon blend fabric is interpreted from a cream-colored brocaded silk gown thought to have been purchased in England in the 1720s for the wedding of Sarah Greene Hill of Wickford, Rhode Island. It is 55″ wide with a 26½″ vertical and 14″ horizontal repeat.

53022   POMEGRANATE

53021   BERRY

53020   GINGER

LIVERPOOL BIRDS

Made of 100 percent cotton, this handsomely textured fabric is reproduced from a white and tan woven cotton textile made in France from about 1795 to 1812. Fabrics of this type often were used for bed hangings with matching window curtains. Liverpool Birds is 52″ wide with a 7″ vertical and 8¾″ horizontal repeat.

131120   VERT

131123   BOIS*

32785   CELADON

136453   CREAM

32786   SAGE GREEN

32782   TURKEY RED

136454   COPENHAGEN

131121   LEMON

*Document denotes color of the antique in the Colonial Williamsburg collection from which the fabric is reproduced. Other colorways are adaptations.

145

PEYTON RANDOLPH WOOL DAMASK

This 100 percent wool fabric is adapted from a yellow worsted damask made in England from about 1750 to 1775. Textiles of this type generally were used for upholstery, valances, and curtains. Peyton Randolph Wool Damask is 52″ wide with a 26″ vertical and horizontal repeat.

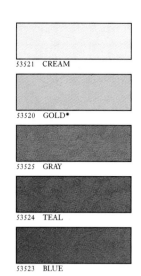

53521   CREAM

53520   GOLD*

53525   GRAY

53524   TEAL

53523   BLUE

53522   RUSSET

HERRINGBONE STRIPE

Woven of silk, cotton, and rayon, this adaptation is based on a bourette silk and hemp textile made about 1750 to 1800. The antique features red and green herringbone stripes alternating with stripes of various blues accented by white and gold. Herringbone Stripe is 50″ wide with an 8½″ horizontal repeat.

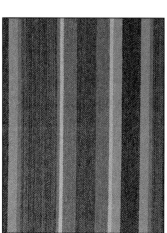

38594   RUST AND BLUE*

BARGELLO

This colorful "Irish stitch" pattern is interpreted in cotton and rayon from a panel of wool embroidered on linen canvas made in New England in 1766. Similar canvas work was used as furniture upholstery. Bargello is 51″ wide with a 15″ vertical and 12¾″ horizontal repeat.

27061   RUST AND BLUE

27060   RED AND GREEN

*Document

WILLIAMSBURG FAUNA
78570   NATURAL
78571   CADET BLUE*
78572   OPAL
78573   JADE
78574   BUTTERCUP

*Document

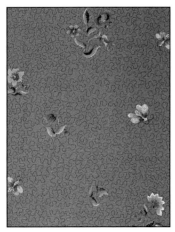

WILLIAMSBURG PETIT FAUNA
78590   NATURAL   78593   JADE
78592   OPAL   78594   BUTTERCUP

WILLIAMSBURG FAUNA STRIPE
78580   NATURAL   78583   JADE
78581   CADET BLUE   78584   BUTTERCUP

CW104 CHAIR, page 66-67.

WILLIAMSBURG FAUNA

Printed on 100 percent cotton, this naturalistic design is interpreted from a chinoiserie needlework panel, circa 1700 to 1720, that was once part of a quilt or valance. Williamsburg Fauna is 54″ wide with a 28″ vertical repeat.

WILLIAMSBURG PETIT FAUNA

Silk embroidered flowers, insects, and Oriental figures are scattered over a quilted ground in the original of this textile, circa 1700 to 1720. This printed 100 percent cotton interpretation is 54″ wide with a 25″ vertical repeat.

WILLIAMSBURG FAUNA STRIPE

This naturalistic design is interpreted from an early eighteenth-century chinoiserie needlework panel. It is printed on 100 percent cotton. Williamsburg Fauna Stripe is 54″ wide with a 25″ vertical repeat.

OPAL

NATURAL

BUTTERCUP

JADE

CADET BLUE

148

Ceremonial chairs such as this one that the governor used at the Capitol were traditionally uphol-stered in luxurious fabric such as silk velvet or damask.

WILLIAMSBURG STRIPE

The original red and green bourette silk and linen textile was made in France from about 1750 to 1800 and was used for upholstery or cur-tains. This silk and cotton Williamsburg Stripe reproduction is 50″ wide.

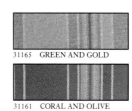

31165   GREEN AND GOLD

31161   CORAL AND OLIVE

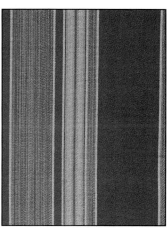

31162   RED AND GREEN*

42380   ROSE BEIGE

42381   SMOKE

WILLIAMSBURG SILK VELVET

In the first half of the eighteenth century, about the time that the deep red original of this European fabric was made, velvet was used for very formal upholstery as well as some clothing. This 100 percent silk reproduction velvet is 50″ wide.

42382   SAGE

42383   AQUAMARINE

42384   SAPPHIRE

42387   FOREST

42386   CRIMSON*

42385   DEEP ROSE

*Document

149

CHINESE PEONY DAMASK

This rich looking damask is reproduced from a brilliant lacquer red silk made in China in the 1740s. It was used for upholstery or women's gowns during this period. Chinese Peony Damask is made of 100 percent silk and is 54″ wide with a 16¾″ vertical repeat.

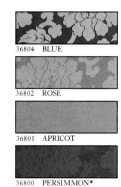

36804   BLUE

36802   ROSE

36805   APRICOT

36800   PERSIMMON*

36803   GOLD

FLEURETTE AND FLEURETTE ADAPTATION

The original blue and white antique silk dress fragment was made in France or England between 1790 and 1810. The woven reproduction is made of 100 percent silk in the document color. The woven adaptations are made of silk and rayon. All are 54″ wide with a 3½″ vertical and horizontal repeat.

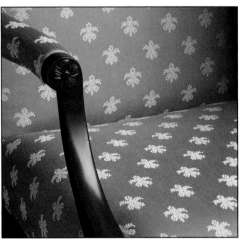

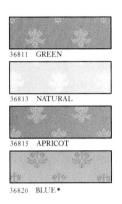

36811   GREEN

36813   NATURAL

36815   APRICOT

36820   BLUE*

36810   ROSE

LUDWELL DAMASK

Made in Europe between 1725 and 1750, the original of this fabric is made of silk in a light and medium blue floral design. Ludwell Damask is adapted in a 100 percent cotton weave. It is 53″ wide with an 18½″ vertical and 26¾″ horizontal repeat.

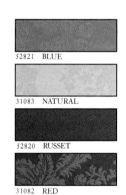

52821   BLUE

31083   NATURAL

52820   RUSSET

31082   RED

52822   SOFT GREEN

BRUSH-EVERARD MOIRÉ STRIPE

The antique eighteenth-century original of this textile was made of bourette silk and cotton and embossed with a watered moiré pattern with red, yellow, cream, and green stripes. It was used for window curtains. This cotton and rayon adaptation is 50″ wide with a 5¼″ horizontal repeat.

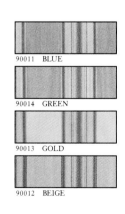

90011   BLUE

90014   GREEN

90013   GOLD

90012   BEIGE

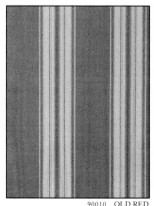

90010   OLD RED

*Document

73790   RED AND BLUE*

BANYAN

Printed in India between 1775 and 1790, the original cotton mordant-painted and dyed chintz was made into a "banyan," a colorful informal loose gown for a man to wear over breeches and shirt. It is reproduced in 100 percent cotton and is 54″ wide with an 18″ vertical repeat.

52842   CORAL

52840   TAFFY

52841   GOLD

52843   SAPPHIRE

GLOUCESTER DAMASK

Made in Europe from about 1680 to 1700, the original patterned gold damask weave was used for formal curtains and chair upholstery. The Gloucester Damask adaptation is made of silk and cotton and is 56″ wide with a 28¼″ vertical and 13⅝″ horizontal repeat.

*Document

The bed furniture in the chamber over the dining room at the Governor's Palace, designated in the Botetourt inventory as "Chints curtains & valens," is made of the Jones toile, or copperplate print, in the purple that was popular with some of Thomas Chippendale's patrons.

JONES TOILE

The original English fabric was copperplate printed in red on white cotton in England about 1761, the date on the copperplate. It typically was used for bed curtains and chair slipcovers. Jones Toile is a printed fabric reproduced in 100 percent cotton. It is 40″ wide with a 77″ vertical repeat.

50090   MOSS GREEN

50098   UMBER

152553   DARK PEWTER

50092   BRICK RED*

152552   TOILE RED

HERRINGBONE STRIÉ

This fabric is adapted from the background of a woven striped textile made about 1750 to 1800. Woven of silk, cotton, and rayon, this fabric was typically used for upholstery and curtains. Herringbone Strié is 50″ wide.

84944   RUST

*Document

153

GLOUCESTER SOLID

This durable fabric is based on an eighteenth-century textile made in America. Originally in a natural color, it was used for everyday purposes such as pillow ticking or grain bags. Gloucester Solid is reproduced in linen and cotton and is 56″ wide.

First Column:

89003	BISCUIT
89019	EMERALD
89014	BISQUE
89015	PERSIMMON
89012	BURNT ORANGE
89013	CINNAMON
89008	COPPER
89007	BRICK RED
89009	CRIMSON

Second Column:

89001	NATURAL
89010	CUSTARD
89000	CREAM*
89011	DAFFODIL
89002	AMBER

89017	PRALINE
89021	MIST GREEN
89024	GRAPE
89005	ROSE
89006	CRANBERRY

Third Column:

89018	FERN
89016	NUTMEG
89022	MOSS
89020	OCEAN GREEN
89023	PEWTER
89026	CADET
89028	MIDNIGHT
89025	ROYAL BLUE
89027	NAVY

*Document

TISSUI FLEURI

The original of this textile is a richly patterned woodblock print made in France about 1790. It features red on a natural cotton tabby ground. Tissui Fleuri is reproduced on linen and cotton and is 54″ wide with an 18″ vertical, 25¼″ horizontal repeat.

161403   TAUPE

161402   FOREST GREEN

161401   CRANBERRY

161404   FRENCH BLUE

161400   RED*

WYTHE HOUSE STRIPE

Used for upholstery or curtains, the dark red monotone striped antique cotton original of this fabric probably was woven in India, circa 1750 to 1800. Wythe House Stripe is reproduced in 100 percent cotton and is 50″ wide with a 6¾″ horizontal repeat.

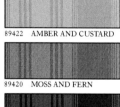

89422   AMBER AND CUSTARD

89420   MOSS AND FERN

89421   EMERALD AND TAUPE

111342   OLD RED*

89424   RED AND BLUE

89423   BLUE AND CINNAMON

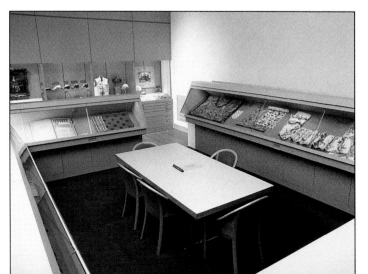

Visitors to the DeWitt Wallace Decorative Arts Gallery may study techniques of production and decoration in the textile study gallery.

*Document

155

WILLIAMSBURG WOOL

Adapted from a blue-green worsted damask made in England between 1700 and 1720, this heavyweight fabric typically was used for upholstery or bed curtains. Williamsburg Wool is adapted from the plain ground areas of this textile. It is woven of 100 percent worsted wool and is 54″ wide.

86057   WILLIAMSBURG BLUE*

FRUIT THEOREM

This interpretive fabric is based on an American theorem painting, possibly from South Carolina, created about 1835. Fruit Theorem is a 100 percent cotton 54″ wide glazed fabric with a 25¼″ vertical repeat.

162831   RED/BLUE

162833   PASTEL

162830   CREAM

162832   RED

162835   BLUE

162834   CAMEL

POMEGRANATE DAMASK

The bold design of the original of this textile was woven of silk in Europe between 1740 and 1790. This adaptation is made of cotton and silk. Pomegranate Damask is 54″ wide with a 34″ vertical and 27″ horizontal repeat.

73731   VANILLA

53732   TEA ROSE

53733   LEAF

53730   RED*

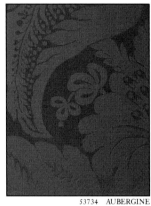

53734   AUBERGINE

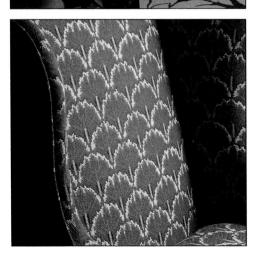

CARNATION NEEDLEWORK

Adapted from an English chair cover needleworked with red wools on linen in the eighteenth century, Carnation Needlework is made of rayon and cotton. It is 51″ wide with a 13¼″ vertical and 8½″ horizontal repeat.

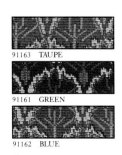

91163   TAUPE

91161   GREEN

91162   BLUE

91160   RED*

*Document

60365   PLUM AND AQUA

60362   RUBY*

60364   BLUE

WILLIAMSBURG FLOWERING TREE

The original of this textile, a handsome block-printed quilt of madder red and penciled blue, was made in England during the last quarter of the eighteenth century. It has been reproduced in a glazed chintz and is 54″ wide with a 34″ vertical repeat.

*Document

The bed curtains in His Lordship's bedchamber at the Palace were of coveted Indian chintz. The colorfast mordant-painted chintzes from India were so popular in England that native textile manufacturers arranged to have them outlawed there, but they were still allowed in the colonies, so Lord Botetourt could enjoy them as a luxury unavailable in his homeland.

WILLIAMSBURG IRIS

The antique copperplate-printed original of this fabric was typically used for bed hangings, window curtains, case covers, or, in this instance, a quilted red cotton counterpane. Williamsburg Iris is a reproduction in 100 percent cotton and is 54″ wide with a 36½″ vertical repeat.

67762   BRONZE

67760   RED*

67761   BLUE

CHERUBINS

Made in England or France between 1790 and 1820, this cotton block-printed fabric typically was used for bed hangings or window curtains. This interpretation is made of glazed 100 percent cotton and is 54″ wide with a 13½″ vertical repeat.

161410   BROWN*

161413   RED AND GREEN

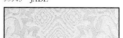

161411   AMETHYST GREEN

161412   BLUE

WILLIAMSBURG GARDEN DAMASK

This cream-colored silk damask probably was made in France about 1750 and was used to make a woman's garment. It is adapted in cotton and is 54″ wide with a 21″ vertical and 13½″ horizontal repeat.

53543   JADE

53542   ROSE

51620   IVORY

51621   SANDALWOOD

51622   APRICOT

51624   SEA

51625   SEAFOAM

53541   BLUE

53540   DELFT

53544   TOFFEE

*Document

159

EDINBURGH CHECK

The blue and white checked linen antique on which this textile is based was used for bed hangings. It was made between 1750 and 1800 in the British Isles. Edinburgh Check is a 48″ wide tightly woven reproduction in 100 percent linen with a 2″ vertical and 1¾″ horizontal repeat.

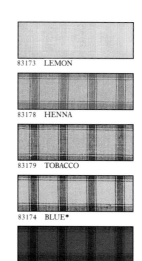

83173   LEMON

83178   HENNA

83179   TOBACCO

83174   BLUE*

83177   BLUE AND RED

83171   VERT

GRAPE ARBOR

Grape Arbor features one element of an American theorem painting made about 1835, possibly in South Carolina. This printed interpretation is made of 100 percent glazed cotton and is 54″ wide with a 25¼″ repeat.

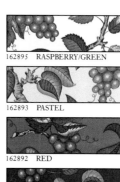

162895   RASPBERRY/GREEN

162893   PASTEL

162892   RED

162894   HUNTER GREEN

162891   PLUM

162890   CREAM

COVERLET COTTON

The original of this textile is a late eighteenth-century or early nineteenth-century American hand-woven and fringed coverlet in white with a repeat pattern of stylized rose motifs. This reproduction is made of heavyweight 100 percent cotton and is 52″ wide.

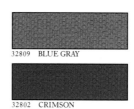

32809   BLUE GRAY

32802   CRIMSON

32804   BLUE

*Document

78730   INDIGO*

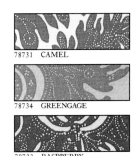

78731   CAMEL

78734   GREENGAGE

78733   RASPBERRY

ONION RESIST

The original of this textile is a resist-printed indigo quilted coverlet probably made in France about 1750 to 1775. Onion Resist is a printed reproduction in 100 percent cotton. It is 54″ wide with a 27″ vertical repeat.

75220   MULTI*

75222   SADDLE TAN

CHINESE FLOWERS

This reproduction chinoiserie design is copied from a woodblock-printed on cotton. The original was made in France about 1785. It is 54″ wide with a 25″ vertical repeat and is made of 100 percent cotton.

66624   SKY BLUE

66622   BRICK RED

66625   INDIGO*

STENCIL FLOWERS

An indigo and white block-printed resist-dyed cotton textile is the original on which this reproduction is based. The antique was made in France between 1750 and 1800. Stencil Flowers is printed on a 54″ wide linen and cotton fabric with a 12½″ vertical and 8½″ horizontal repeat.

*Document

An antique quilted counter-pane of blue resist warms the bed of one of Thomas Everard's daughters.

DIAMOND MAZE

This colorful pattern is interpreted from a panel of wool embroidered on linen canvas made in New England in 1766. It is made of 100 percent cotton. Diamond Maze is 58″ wide with a 29½″ vertical repeat.

78403   INDIGO

CW307 CHAIR, page 71.

WYTHE HOUSE BORDER RESIST

An indigo resist-printed cotton made in England or America, circa 1740 to 1760, is the basis for this reproduction. This fabric originally was used as bed hangings. This reproduction is printed on 100 percent cotton. It is 50″ long with a 28″ vertical repeat.

162380   BLUE*

*Document

163

CW129   SOFA, page 62.

PLEASURES OF THE FARM

The original of this fabric features a series of farm life scenes plate-printed in purple on tabby-woven cotton. It was made in Jouy, France, circa 1785 to 1790, and typically was used for bed curtains or slipcovers in the bedchamber. This reproduction is printed on 40″ wide 100 percent cotton and has a 40″ vertical repeat.

50420   YELLOW OCHRE

50422   REGIMENTAL RED

50424   COLONIAL BLUE

50428   ROYAL PURPLE*

74254   MOONSTONE BLUE

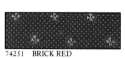

74251   BRICK RED

74252   SPRUCE

74255   RED

74250   BLUE.*

PARSLEY

The original of such a small scale block print was used primarily for clothing. This textile is based on one of 347 swatches found in a Dutch sample book dating from 1790 to 1820. Parsley is a 54″ wide printed reproduction on 100 percent cotton with a 6″ vertical repeat.

*Document

PONDICHERRY

Made in India for the export market about 1770 to 1795, the original of this block-printed, mordant-painted, and dyed fabric was used for women's clothing and bed hangings. Pondicherry is a printed reproduction on 54″ wide 100 percent cotton with a 17½″ vertical repeat.

65102   LAVENDER AND PINK*

65100   RED

65106   MOONSTONE BLUE AND PINK

POTPOURRI

A block-printed red, brown, and blue center block for a quilt is the antique from which this fabric is derived. The original was made on tabby-woven cotton in England about 1815. This printed adaptation is made of 100 percent cotton. It is 54″ wide with a 26½″ vertical repeat.

64975   BUFF*

64974   OLD ROSE

64977   MOONSTONE BLUE

64971   NATURAL

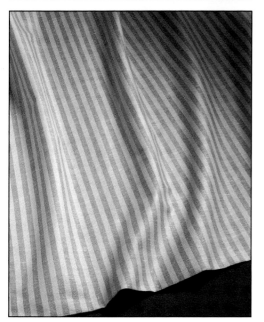

WILLIAMSBURG LINEN STRIPE

The eighteenth-century mustard and blue striped original of this fabric was made in America with a wool weft and linen warp. Williamsburg Linen Stripe is a woven reproduction on 48″ cotton and linen with a 1″ horizontal repeat.

86550   SAND

86552   FERN

86553   BOTTLE GREEN

86555   MEDIUM BLUE

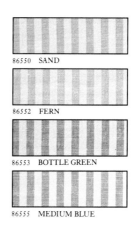

86554   CADET

*Document

CW43 CHAIR, page 70.

LEATHER

Leather was hand-produced in both Virginia and England and came in a variety of colors. In Williamsburg, leather was sold by the local harness and saddle-maker, Alexander Craig. It most commonly was used on seating that needed to take wear and tear and was ideal in dining rooms and passages because it could be wiped clean. Leather is handsomely glazed for a luxurious feeling to the touch.

WG2520   BLACK CALUMET

WG2233   PYRACANTHA

WG2272   CALUMET

WG2506   ALLSPICE

WG2164   ALE

WG2524   POWDER HORN

WG2223   EVERGREEN

WG2248   SHREWSBURY STONE

WG2271   BURGESS BLUE

WG2038   FARRIER

MILL HALL COVERLET

The source of this interpretive fabric is a single-woven jacquard rose and aqua wool coverlet made in Clinton County, Pennsylvania, about 1850. Mill Hall Coverlet is woven of 54″ 100 percent cotton fabric with a 28½″ vertical repeat.

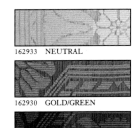
162933 NEUTRAL

162930 GOLD/GREEN

162932 INDIGO/PLUM

162931 ROSE/AQUA

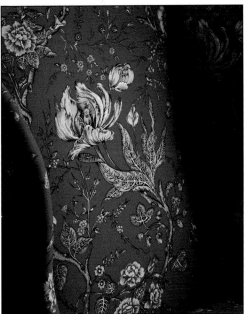

FLORIBUNDA

This textile is based on a French antique, circa 1785 to 1800, using block-printed, multicolored naturalistic flowers on a muddy colored cotton ground. It was used typically for bed hangings, curtains, and slipcovers. Floribunda is a printed reproduction on 54″ 100 percent cotton with a 27″ vertical repeat.

78752 BRICK RED

78751 BLUE/PERSIMMON

78755 RAW UMBER

78750 TOBACCO*

78754 SHUTTER GREEN

78756 CARNATION

FOX GRAPE

This interpretive fabric is based on a fragment of original wallpaper found on the walls of a closet in the Nicolson Shop at Williamsburg. Thomas Jefferson ordered wallpaper with a "Lattice or trellis" from Paris in 1790. Fox Grape is printed on glazed 100 percent cotton. It is 54″ wide with a 18″ vertical repeat.

163533 AUTUMN ROSE

163532 IVORY

163530 TAN

163531 BLUE

163534 AQUA MIST

*Document

TAVERN CHECK

This fabric is reproduced from an indigo and white checked linen slipcover made in America between 1750 and 1800. Tavern Check is woven of 54″ wide cotton and linen with a 3″ vertical and horizontal repeat.

81503   SAGE
81501   GOLD
81509   HUNTER GREEN
81502   COLONIAL RED

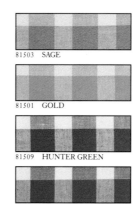

81508   BLUE*

SHIR O'SHAKKAR

Made in Britain, America, or possibly in India for export, the antique on which this fabric is based is a blue and white cotton seersucker that was used typically for bed curtains and window hangings. Shir O'Shakkar is a woven reproduction of 54″ wide 100 percent cotton with a 2″ horizontal repeat.

81573   NATURAL
81571   OCHRE
81576   QUARTZ
81572   RED

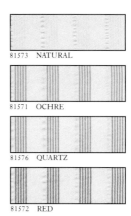

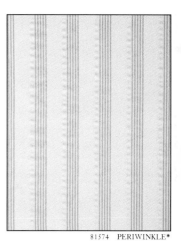

81574   PERIWINKLE*

RALEIGH TAVERN RESIST

This textile is reproduced from a late eighteenth-century French blue resist-dyed cotton bedspread. Raleigh Tavern Resist is printed on 54″ wide linen and cotton with a 42″ vertical repeat.

178161   ADAM GOLD
62905   BRICK RED
178162   RED

178164   BLUE*

*Document

INDIAN CHINTZ

This fabric is reproduced from an eighteenth-century or early nineteenth-century cotton chintz made on the Coromandel Coast of India or in Batavia, Java, under Dutch patronage. Its high glaze is achieved with rice starch and polishing. Indian Chintz is a printed reproduction in 54" wide glazed cotton with an 8½" vertical repeat.

162943   PASTEL

162942   GREEN/RED

162944   RED/CAMEL

162941   BLUE/YELLOW

162940   RED AND BLUE*

CHECKS

Possibly used as a coverlet, the tan and white American original of this reproduction fabric was woven of homespun linen in the early nineteenth century. Checks is woven of linen and cotton and is 48" wide with a ¾" vertical and horizontal repeat.

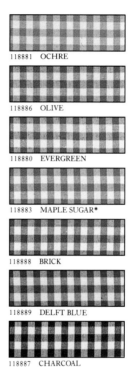

118881   OCHRE

118886   OLIVE

118880   EVERGREEN

118883   MAPLE SUGAR*

118888   BRICK

118889   DELFT BLUE

118887   CHARCOAL

118884   DARK BLUE

FINCH STENCIL

This intepretive fabric is based on a floor cloth in a painting by John Brewster, Jr. Completed about 1800, the painting features a boy with a yellow finch perched on his index finger. Finch Stencil is printed on 54" wide 100 percent glazed cotton with a 1" repeat.

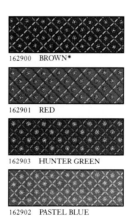

162900   BROWN*

162901   RED

162903   HUNTER GREEN

162902   PASTEL BLUE

162904   MIDNIGHT BLUE

*Document

Information on all fabrics shown above can be found on the opposite page.

These four designs are part of an exciting new collection of printed fabrics from F. Schumacher & Co. Twelve coordinating patterns will include fabrics of cotton, cotton/linen blends, and glazed cotton. New colorways will be presented for some fabrics that were first introduced in the 1950s. Other fabrics, developed to complement companion wallpapers, will be introduced for the first time. These new printed fabrics include Fox Grape, Portsmouth Pineapple, Brighton, and Chinese Peony.

All twelve patterns are characterized by a classic style that will endure throughout ever-changing design trends. Their coordinating patterns and colorways will create a multitude of exciting design possibilities for furniture, accessories, window treatments, and even wallcoverings.

NEEDLEWORK BOUQUET

This interpretive fabric is based on a needlework coverlet embroidered of silk on linen in England, circa 1720-1750. Needlework Bouquet is printed on glazed 100 percent cotton. It is 54″ wide with a 12⅝″ vertical repeat.

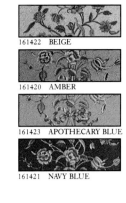

161422   BEIGE

161420   AMBER

161423   APOTHECARY BLUE

161421   NAVY BLUE

161424   CREAM

PURSELINER

Interpreted from a deep blue English wool-flocked wallpaper made about 1740 to 1770, Purseliner is printed on glazed 100 percent cotton. It is 54″ wide.

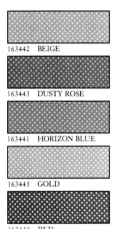

163442   BEIGE

163443   DUSTY ROSE

163441   HORIZON BLUE

163445   GOLD

163440   RED

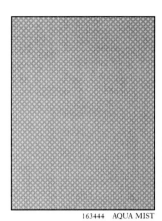

163444   AQUA MIST

LARCHMONT

The original of this adaptation fabric was made in England between 1780 and 1810 and typically was used for upholstery. It is printed on 52″ wide 100 percent cotton with a 6½″ horizontal repeat.

163552   BEIGE

163553   DUSTY ROSE

163554   AQUA MIST

163555   GOLD

163550   RED*

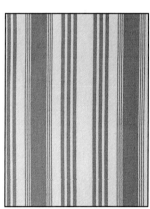

163551   HORIZON BLUE

FLORAL STRIPE

The reproduction fabric is based on linen and cotton quilted curtains and bed hangings block-printed in France about 1785 to 1810. It is printed on 100 percent cotton and is 52″ wide with a 12½″ vertical repeat.

163602   BEIGE

163604   AQUA MIST

163601   HORIZON BLUE

163605   GOLD

163600   RED

163603   DUSTY ROSE

*Document

DOBBY WEAVE

The natural linen warp and weft of this fabric are woven in a fancy twill pattern that was used typically for table linens and towels. The original of this reproduction was made in America between 1780 and 1820. Dobby Weave is woven of 54" wide 100 percent cotton.

91867 TAUPE

91866 SANDSTONE

81729 OFF WHITE*

91865 WHITE

91864 ECRU

91863 DUSTY ROSE

91862 CORAL

91861 BRICK RED

91860 TEA ROSE

91858 RED

91857 LACQUER

91856 BURGUNDY

91855 ROSEDUST

Shown clockwise from top left:
91840 CELADON
91833 MOCHA
91847 MEDIUM BLUE
91859 WATERMELON
91853 AUBERGINE

*Document

81726 CAFE AU LAIT
91834 TOPAZ
91832 BROWN
91831 PERSIMMON
91830 RUSSET
81728 COPPER

81731 BISCUIT
91835 YELLOW
91836 LEAF
91837 GREEN
91838 IVY
91839 JADE

91846 COPENHAGEN
91845 WEDGWOOD
91844 CADET
91843 AQUA
91842 TURQUOISE
91841 EVERGREEN

91848 ROYAL
91849 NAVY
91850 BRISTOL
91851 PERIWINKLE
91852 MARINE
91854 DUSK

COUNTRY GARDEN

This lovely printed textile is interpreted from a cotton white on white needlework counterpane begun in 1812 and signed "Alexander & Salley B. Fulcher, 1818." Country Garden is 54″ wide with a 25¼″ vertical repeat and is made of 100 percent cotton.

77121   MULTI ON PARCHMENT

77123   CUIVRE

77122   FRENCH BLUE/PINK

TALCOTT STRIPE

A painting from about 1832 by Deborah Goldsmith showing Venetian carpeting is the source for this interpretive fabric. Talcott rugs also have been developed based on this painting. Talcott Stripe is 54″ wide and is made of linen and cotton.

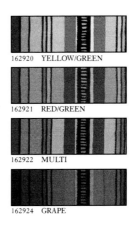

162920   YELLOW/GREEN

162921   RED/GREEN

162922   MULTI

162924   GRAPE

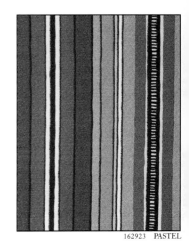

162923   PASTEL

FLORAL APPLIQUÉ

The distinctive black ground of this fabric is interpreted from a reverse-appliquéd table cover probably made in New York between 1830 and 1845. Floral Appliqué is printed on 100 percent cotton. It is 54″ wide with a 25¼″ vertical repeat.

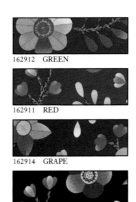

162912   GREEN

162911   RED

162914   GRAPE

162910   BLACK

162913   PASTEL

TRACERY FLORAL

Typically used for bedchamber furnishings such as bed hangings and slipcovers, the original of this fabric is a colorful block-printed linen and cotton French textile made from about 1775 to 1800. Tracery Floral is reproduced in 54″ wide 100 percent cotton with a 13″ vertical repeat.

73783 SPRUCE AND TAN

73780 RED*

WILLIAMSBURG WOOL MOREEN

The original of this fabric is adapted from a wool and mohair textile woven in England, circa 1750 to 1800. It was used for upholstery, curtains, and bed hangings. Williamsburg Wool Moreen is woven of wool and cotton in a 50″ width.

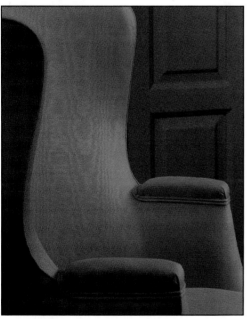

90343 CUSTARD

90344 GOLD

90345 CYPRUS

90346 GREEN*

90347 BAYBERRY

90348 CADET

90349 ROYAL

90342 SIENNA

90341 BRICK

90340 BURGUNDY

WILLIAMSBURG MULTI-STRIPE

Typically used for furniture upholstery, the original of this reproduction fabric was made in England from about 1780 to 1810. It was made of wool and cotton in a red and white chevron twill weave. Williamsburg Multi-Stripe is woven of 52″ wide cotton with a 6½″ horizontal repeat.

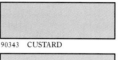

132962 RED*

51290 ROSE DUST AND WHITE

51291 RUST AND CREAM

81481 OCHRE

81485 YELLOW

132964 BLUE

51292 CAPRI AND WHITE

81489 BLACK AND WHITE

*Document

FOX GRAPE REPRODUCTION WALLPAPER, this section.

WALLPAPER
IN THE EIGHTEENTH CENTURY

For the past three centuries wallpaper has been a fashionable and highly visible option in interior decorating schemes. Although there is little documentation for its use in Virginia before the middle of the eighteenth century, wallpaper became relatively popular during the second half of the century. An advertisement in the *Virginia Gazette* by Benjamin Bucktrout (1771) illustrates the wide variety of papers available for sale in Williamsburg:

> Just IMPORTED . . . A NEAT and ELEGANT ASSORTMENT of PAPER HANGINGS, . . . of the newest fashions, . . . namely embossed, Stucco, Chintz, Striped, Mosaick, Damask, and common.

While papers were available for purchase in Williamsburg, some local residents ordered wallpaper directly from London. Early orders specify such papers as "a blue ground with large yellow flowers" or "neat handsome paper hangings Green ground." Colonials relied heavily on their London merchants to supply them, not only with a paper of suitable style, but with an appropriate color as well.

Another fashionable treatment, plain colored paper with borders around the edges, was introduced into Williamsburg by the royal governor, Lord Botetourt. The opulent effect was immediately copied by many Virginians as evidenced by an order placed by Robert Beverley in 1771:

> I have been some time employed in building an House, and as I am desirous of fitting it up in a plain neat Manner, I would willingly consult the present Fashion, for that foolish Passion has made its way, Even into this remote Region. I observ'd that Lord B[otetourt] had hung a room with plain blue paper . . . which I thought had a pretty effect.

Affluent Virginians wished to furnish their houses in the latest fashion and, as Beverley suggested, were strongly influenced by the "plain neat Manner." The borders that adorned plain papered walls were often made of papier-mâché, which gave the appearance of carved wood. As the century progressed, printed borders also became fashionable, and were applied to a variety of patterns.

— MARGARET B. PRITCHARD
Curator of Prints and Maps

BRIGHTON

WALLPAPER
REPRODUCTIONS

Despite the fact that wallpaper was used extensively in eighteenth- and nineteenth-century decoration, its poor survival rate has made the study of wallpaper more elusive than many other aspects of interior decoration. Once worn or out of fashion, it was either discarded or papered over. Therefore, many sources are relied upon for the study of wallpaper.

Prints and paintings yield vital evidence about specific wallpapers and colors, and they also indicate which patterns were considered appropriate for various locations in the home. Newspaper advertisements and private orders reveal which styles were fashionable in various geographic regions. The primary sources for study, however, are the surviving fragments of papers themselves, which museums have fervently collected over the years. Many of our wallpapers have been reproduced from surviving fragments on which the entire repeat of the design is intact. For other papers, we have followed in the tradition of eighteenth- and nineteenth-century manufacturers, basing our designs on popular textile patterns of the period.

— MARGARET B. PRITCHARD
Curator of Prints and Maps

BRIGHTON

A fascination with the Orient was prevalent in eighteenth-century England and the colonies. This wallpaper is adapted from a block-printed hand-colored original made about 1785. It is vinyl coated and strippable with a pre-trimmed 27″ width, 36″ vertical repeat, and half drop match.

BERKELEY SQUARE

BERKELEY SQUARE

This pattern is adapted from an antique wallpaper made between 1840 and 1860. It was discovered during the restoration of a house on the Eastern Shore of Virginia. The original was hand-blocked and applied to the wall in small square sheets. This adaptation is vinyl coated and strippable with a pretrimmed 27″ width, 13½″ vertical repeat, and half drop match.

PRINCESS ANNE

This wallpaper is interpreted from a fabric swatch from a Dutch merchant's sample book dating between 1790 and 1820. It employs the full two-stripe pattern of the antique. Princess Anne is vinyl coated and strippable with a 27″ pretrimmed width, 5¼″ vertical repeat, and straight across match.

LAFAYETTE FLORAL

The original of this charming reproduction pattern was discovered under several layers of wallpapers in an American house, the earliest part of which was built about 1757. This reproduction pattern is vinyl coated and strippable with a 20½″ pretrimmed width, 22″ vertical repeat, and straight across match.

By the last quarter of the eighteenth century wallpaper appears frequently in prints of interiors, suggesting its increasing popularity as a form of decoration.

PRINCESS ANNE

LAFAYETTE FLORAL

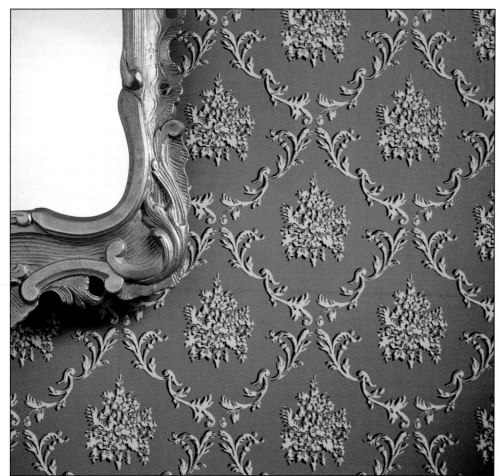

BRUSH EVERARD

BRUSH EVERARD

Wallpaper fragments of this design were discovered during restoration of the Brush-Everard House in Williamsburg. Today, this reproduction is used in the same room where the original was found. Brush Everard is vinyl coated and strippable with a 27″ pretrimmed width, 11″ vertical repeat, and half drop match.

CASTLE HILL

CASTLE HILL

This wallpaper is interpreted from a fragment of brocade silk taffeta made in England or France, circa 1765 to 1780. Extra weft threads were often woven into the multicolored fabric to form designs that appear to stand out in slight relief. Castle Hill is over-printed to give the same effect. It is vinyl coated and strippable with a 27″ pretrimmed width, 14¼″ vertical repeat, and straight across match.

WINTERBERRY

This wallpaper is reproduced from an antique found in a late eighteenth-century home in Melrose, Massachusetts. Winterberry is vinyl coated and strippable with a 27″ pre-trimmed width, 11″ vertical repeat, and straight across match.

WINTERBERRY

BURDETTE

This interpretive wallpaper is based on a block-printed fabric which dates from 1740 to 1780. The fabric was woven and printed in England or on the Continent and used as a bed valance. The flower and scallop motifs on this wallpaper are similar to designs found on antique papers after about 1780. Burdette is vinyl coated and strippable with a 27″ pre-trimmed width, 12⁹/₁₆″ vertical repeat, and straight across match.

BURDETTE

CHINESE PEONY

CHINESE PEONY

This adaptation is based on a rare hand-painted wallpaper made in eighteenth-century China. It features birds, butterflies, and dragonflies as well as the graceful peony, the flower of the seasons that symbolizes spring in China. Chinese Peony is vinyl coated and strippable with a 27″ pretrimmed width, 36″ vertical repeat, and half drop match.

FOX GRAPE

FOX GRAPE

This wallpaper is reproduced from an original found on the walls in a closet of the Nicolson Store in Williamsburg. Thomas Jefferson ordered wallpaper with a "lattice or trellis" design from Paris in 1790. Fox Grape is vinyl coated and strippable with a 27″ pretrimmed width, 19″ vertical repeat, and half drop match.

PONDICHERRY

This interpretive wallpaper is from a fabric made in India for the export market between 1770 and 1795. The original textile was used for women's clothing and bed hangings. Pondicherry is vinyl coated and strippable with a 27″ pre-trimmed width, 25½″ vertical repeat, and straight across match.

PONDICHERRY

PORTSMOUTH PINEAPPLE

The pineapple was a rare and costly fruit in the colonies and symbolized the spirit of hospitality. As such, it was a popular and recurring design motif. This wallpaper is an adaptation of an original of the period. It is vinyl coated and strippable with a 27″ pre-trimmed width, 14¼″ vertical repeat, and half drop match.

PORTSMOUTH PINEAPPLE

185

PINSTRIPE

COCKLESHELLS

SHELL BORDER

COCKLESHELLS

The shell motif was a popular element in eighteenth-century furniture design. Cockleshells was interpreted from the carved shell detail at the top of a gilded looking glass made in England, circa 1710-1730. This wallpaper is pretrimmed, vinyl coated, and strippable with a 3″ vertical repeat. Cockleshells is available in blue, pink, beige, mint reverse, and yellow.

Blue	50-1195-4
Pink	50-1195-5
Beige	50-1195-2
Mint	50-1195-3
Yellow	50-1195-9

SHELL BORDER

This border wallpaper also is inspired by the carved shell detail at the top of an eighteenth-century looking glass. It is vinyl coated and strippable with a $2\frac{1}{8}''$ horizontal repeat. Shell Border is available in blue, pink, beige, mint reverse, and yellow.

Blue	50-1210-4
Pink	50-1210-5
Beige	50-1210-2
Mint	50-1210-3
Yellow	50-1210-9

PURSELINER

PINSTRIPE

ANNABELLE

PURSELINER

This diminutive print is interpreted from the background motif of an antique wallpaper of French or English origin, circa 1750-1760. It is pretrimmed, vinyl coated, and strippable with a straight match white pattern on a beige, blue, mint, mustard, pink, or rose background.

Beige	50-1208-2
Blue	50-1208-4
Mint	50-1208-3
Mustard	50-1208-1
Pink	50-1208-5
Rose	50-1208-6

PIN STRIPE

A fabric swatch from a merchant's sample book was the source for this interpretive wallpaper. The book was published by J. J. Jourdain of London, England, between 1777 and 1786, and contains more than 1,500 samples of fabric generally used for clothing during the period. Pin Stripe is pretrimmed, vinyl coated, and strippable with a random match pattern.

Blue on Blue (Dark)	50-1197-7
Beige on White	50-1197-8
Mint on Mint	50-1197-0
Coral on Coral	50-1197-6
*Shown on Page 186	
*Blue on Blue (Light)	50-1197-4
*Pink on Beige	50-1197-5
*Beige on Beige	50-1197-2
*Mint on Beige	50-1197-3
*Yellow on Yellow	50-1197-9

ANNABELLE

A fragment of block-printed cotton textile, possibly made in provincial France about 1786-1793, is the source for this interpretive wallpaper. The antique textile features a pink and red patterned ground with pairs of undulating white floral vines. Annabelle is pretrimmed, vinyl coated, and strippable with a straight match white pattern on a coral, mint, beige, or blue background.

Coral	50-1182-6
Mint	50-1182-0
Beige	50-1182-8
Blue	50-1182-7

TIDEWATER STRIPE

A homespun striped linen and wool blanket is the inspiration for this interpretive wallpaper. The original features blue stripes on a buff background. Tidewater Stripe is pretrimmed, vinyl coated, and strippable with a random match. The gold stripes alternate with rose, mint, white, red, or blue stripes.

Rose with Cream	50-1185-2
Mint with Gold	50-1185-3
White with Gold	50-1185-0
Red with Gold	50-1185-5
Blue with Gold	50-1185-4

STAR BORDER

A textile in a Dutch merchant's sample book is the source for this interpreted wallpaper. The book dates from between 1790 and 1820. This border is vinyl coated and strippable with a $3\frac{5}{8}''$ horizontal repeat.

Blue	50-1204-4
Rose Reverse	50-1204-2
Beige Reverse	50-1204-0
Mint	50-1204-3
Red	50-1204-5

STARS

This tiny print is interpreted from a swatch of cotton fabric in a Dutch sample book from the late eighteenth or early nineteenth century. The original fabric features slightly larger white stars on a blue background. Stars is pretrimmed, vinyl coated, and strippable with a straight match. It is available with gold stars on a blue, cream, white, mint, or red background.

Blue	50-1191-4
Cream	50-1191-2
White	50-1191-0
Mint	50-1191-3
Red	50-1191-5

STAR BORDER

Textile merchants, tailors, and upholsterers used fabric sample books to display their wares to potential customers. These small prints were interpreted from textiles in such a book published in Holland between 1790 and 1820. The book contained 347 samples of mostly cotton fabric with small repetitive floral and geometric patterns.

COFFEE BEAN

Pretrimmed, vinyl coated, and strippable with a straight match.

Brown	50-1187-9
Mint Reverse	50-1187-3
Beige	50-1187-2
Blue	50-1187-4
Red	50-1187-5

WIDGETS

Pretrimmed, vinyl coated, and strippable with a $3\frac{1}{8}''$ vertical repeat.

Red	50-1189-5
Blue	50-1189-4
Beige Reverse	50-1189-2
Mint	50-1189-3
Brown	50-1189-9

IVY

Pretrimmed, vinyl coated, and strippable.

Mint	50-1205-3
Rose	50-1205-6
Blue	50-1205-4
Mustard	50-1205-1

WILD GRAPE

Pretrimmed, vinyl coated, and strippable with a straight match and $11\frac{3}{4}''$ vertical repeat.

Red on Beige	50-1190-5
Blue on White	50-1190-4
Mint Reverse	50-1190-3
Beige Reverse	50-1190-2

WILLIAMSBURG CHECK

A mid-eighteenth-century linen textile is the source of inspiration for this interpretive wallpaper and coordinating border. The antique features a fine weave and crisp detail. This wallpaper is pretrimmed, vinyl coated, and strippable with a straight match.

Blue	50-1179-4
Mint	50-1179-3
Beige	50-1179-2
Brown	50-1179-9
Red	50-1179-5

CHECK BORDER

Blue	50-1180-4
Mint	50-1180-3
Beige	50-1180-2
Brown	50-1180-9
Red	50-1180-5

COFFEE BEAN

WIDGETS

CHECK

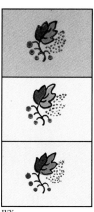

IVY

WILD GRAPE

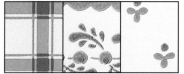

Shown top to bottom: Chatham, Mistletoe Border, Jamestown Check

CHATHAM

This modern adaptation is based on the background motif of a wallpaper dating from about 1800. Small, simple patterns such as these sometimes were called "domino papers" after a group of French craftsmen who specialized in making them. Chatham is pretrimmed, vinyl coated, and strippable with a straight match.

Green w/Pink	50-1207-3	Blue w/Beige	50-1207-4
Yellow w/Green	50-1207-1	Red w/Blue	50-1207-5

MISTLETOE BORDER

Ornamental border papers were very fashionable in the late eighteenth and entire nineteenth century. This adaptation is based on one of three motifs adapted from an antique wallpaper, circa 1800. It is vinyl coated and strippable, with a $\frac{3}{4}''$ horizontal repeat.

Mint w/Pink	50-1201-3	Blue w/Tan	50-1201-4
Green w/Yellow	50-1201-1	Red w/Blue	50-1201-5

JAMESTOWN CHECK

Checks were popular as an upholstery fabric during the later eighteenth century. A set of blue and white linen bedhangings, probably made in England between 1750 and 1800, was the inspiration for this interpretive wallpaper. Jamestown Check is pretrimmed, vinyl coated, and strippable with a straight match.

Mint	50-1194-3	Blue	50-1194-4
Yellow	50-1194-1	Red w/Blue	50-1194-5

ROSEWELL

This wallpaper is interpreted from the background of a textile in J. J. Jourdain's fabric sample book, represented by the companion wallpaper, Cary. Rosewell is pretrimmed, vinyl coated, and strippable with a straight match.

Pink	50-1184-5	Blue	50-1184-4
Gold	50-1184-1	Beige	50-1184-2

CARY

This wallpaper is interpreted from a fabric swatch in a clothing fabric sample book published in London, England, by J. J. Jourdain between 1777 and 1786. Cary is pretrimmed, vinyl coated, and strippable with a straight match.

Pink	50-1183-5	Blue	50-1183-4
Gold	50-1183-1	Beige	50-1183-2

Shown top to bottom: Rosewell, Cary

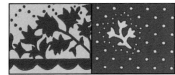
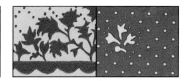

PARSLEY

This small print is interpreted from one of 347 swatches of mostly cotton fabric in a merchant's sample book published in Holland between 1790 and 1820. Parsley is pretrimmed, vinyl coated, and strippable with a straight match.

Teal	50-1203-2	Red Reverse	50-1203-5
Blue	50-1203-4	Green Reverse	50-1203-3

ARBOR BORDER

The scalloped stripe on this adaptation border is one of the decorative devices featured on an original antique wallpaper, circa 1800. Arbor Border is vinyl coated and strippable with a 6¼″ horizontal repeat.

Teal Reverse	50-1202-2	Red	50-1202-5
Blue	50-1202-4	Green	50-1202-3

KENT

This wallpaper is adapted from a textile in a Dutch merchant's sample book, circa 1790-1820. It is pretrimmed, vinyl coated, and strippable with a 1¹⁄₁₆″ vertical repeat.

Pink Reverse	50-1193-6	Red	50-1193-7
Blue	50-1193-1	Mint	50-1193-9
Beige Reverse	50-1193-8		

FLORAL BORDER

This decorative border is adapted from a block-printed linen fabric from France, circa 1785-1800. The original featured a red floral design on a natural ground. Floral Border is vinyl coated and strippable with a 1¼″ horizontal repeat.

Pink	50-1181-6	Red	50-1181-7
Blue	50-1181-1	Mint	50-1181-9
Beige	50-1181-8		

TIDEWATER STRIPE

This striking striped wallpaper adaptation is inspired by a homespun eighteenth-century linen and wool blanket. The original featured blue stripes on a buff background. Tidewater Stripe is pretrimmed, vinyl coated, and strippable with a random match.

Pink with White	50-1185-6	Red	50-1185-7
Blue	50-1185-1	Mint	50-1185-9
Beige	50-1185-8		

Shown top to bottom: Parsley, Arbor Border, Parsley

Shown top to bottom: Kent, Floral Border, Tidewater Stripe

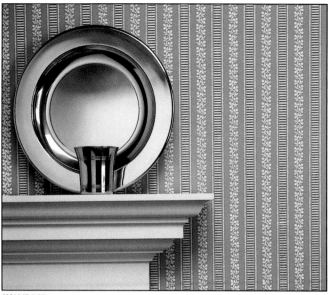

SHAMROCK

SHAMROCK

This wallpaper is interpreted from one of 1,500 fabric swatches in a sample book published by J.J. Jourdain of London, England, between 1777 and 1786. Shamrock is pretrimmed, vinyl coated, and strippable with a random match.

Blue	50-1196-4
Tan	50-1196-2
Red	50-1196-5
Mint	50-1196-3

COTTAGE STENCIL

COTTAGE STENCIL

This interpretive wallpaper is inspired by one of 347 fabrics in a Dutch sample book, circa 1790-1820, featuring small repetitive florals and geometric patterns. Cottage Stencil is pretrimmed, vinyl coated, and strippable with a straight match.

Mint	50-1186-3
Tan	50-1186-2
Red	50-1186-5
Blue	50-1186-7
Blue Reverse	50-1186-4

AMELIA

AMELIA

This colorful wallpaper is interpreted from a fragment of block-printed cotton fabric made in France about 1800. The original featured a floral design with undulating bands punctuated by pink horizontal stripes. Amelia is pretrimmed, vinyl coated, and strippable with a $6\frac{5}{16}''$ vertical repeat. It is available with a dominant color of blue, pink, or rust.

Blue	50-1198-4
Pink	50-1198-5
Rust	50-1198-6

INDIENNE PRINT

This intricately patterned wallpaper is interpreted from a block-printed cotton textile fragment made in India or France between 1790 and 1830. Indienne Print is pretrimmed, vinyl coated, and strippable with a 9″ vertical repeat. It is available with a dominant color of pink, rust, blue, or pink on dark blue.

Pink	50-1200-5
Rust	50-1200-6
Blue	50-1200-4
Pink on Dark Blue	50-1200-7

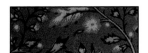

INDIENNE PRINT

CHARLOTTE

This interpretive wallpaper was inspired from a block-printed cotton and linen textile made in France between 1786 and 1790. The original featured a red and black floral design on a natural linen ground. Charlotte is pretrimmed, vinyl coated, and strippable with an 8⅝″ vertical repeat.

Red on beige	50-1206-5
Gold on beige	50-1206-1
Blue on white	50-1206-4
Teal on beige	50-1206-3

CHARLOTTE

TINY TULIPS

This diminutive print is adapted from an antique endpaper in the Colonial Williamsburg collection. These decorative endpapers were often used inside book covers, or to line trunks and boxes. Tiny Tulips is pretrimmed, vinyl coated, and strippable with a straight match.

Red Reverse	50-1178-5
Yellow Reverse	50-1178-1
Pink	50-1178-7
Red	50-1178-2
Blue	50-1178-0
Blue Reverse	50-1178-4

TINY TULIPS

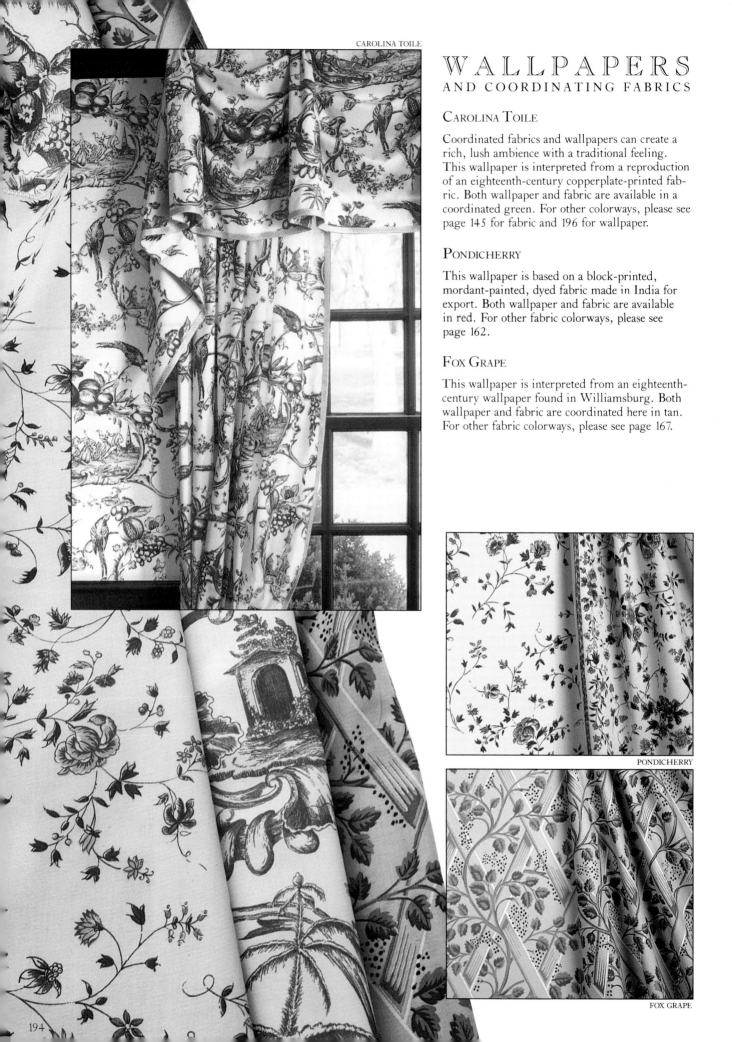

WALLPAPERS
AND COORDINATING FABRICS

CAROLINA TOILE

Coordinated fabrics and wallpapers can create a rich, lush ambience with a traditional feeling. This wallpaper is interpreted from a reproduction of an eighteenth-century copperplate-printed fabric. Both wallpaper and fabric are available in a coordinated green. For other colorways, please see page 145 for fabric and 196 for wallpaper.

PONDICHERRY

This wallpaper is based on a block-printed, mordant-painted, dyed fabric made in India for export. Both wallpaper and fabric are available in red. For other fabric colorways, please see page 162.

FOX GRAPE

This wallpaper is interpreted from an eighteenth-century wallpaper found in Williamsburg. Both wallpaper and fabric are coordinated here in tan. For other fabric colorways, please see page 167.

PONDICHERRY

FOX GRAPE

WILLIAMSBURG CHECK

PURSELINER

PARSLEY

The custom of decorating rooms en suite, *or with matching fabric on walls and upholstery, was popular from the seventeenth century. By the mid-eighteenth century wallpaper offered a cheaper alternative to fabric on walls. In this 1781 print similar stripes unify the walls, settee, and side chair.*

MASTER LAVENDER *qualifying himself for the* ARMY.

WILLIAMSBURG CHECK

This wallpaper is interpreted from an eighteenth-century linen textile. Both wallpaper and fabric are available in a coordinated red or blue. For other colorways and item numbers, please see page 189 for wallpaper and 171 for fabric.

PURSELINER

In the eighteenth century, fabrics were selected from swatches from a sample book. This wallpaper is taken from just such a book from Holland. Both are coordinated here in beige, blue, or mint. For other colorways and item numbers, please see page 187 for wallpaper and 173 for fabric.

FLORAL STRIPE fabric with KENT, FLORAL BORDER, TIDEWATER STRIPE wallpapers.

PARSLEY

This small print is based on fabric swatches from a Dutch merchant's sample book. Both are coordinated in a handsome red, blue, or green reverse. For other colorways and item numbers, please see page 191 for wallpaper and 164 for fabric.

KENT, FLORAL BORDER, AND TIDEWATER STRIPE

This combination of small print interpretive wallpapers and fabrics can be mixed and matched to create a variety of informal looks. Shown here in beige, blue, and mint. For other colorways and item numbers, please see page 191 for wallpapers and 173 for fabric.

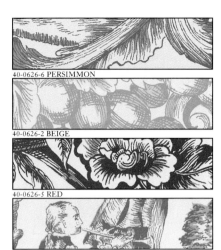

40-0626-6 PERSIMMON

40-0626-2 BEIGE

40-0626-5 RED

40-0626-4 BLUE

CAROLINA TOILE

This wallpaper is taken from a copperplate-printed cotton and linen counterpane made in England in the late eighteenth century. This type of design often pictured vignettes of country life and pastoral scenes. Carolina Toile measures 26″ wide with a 36″ vertical repeat and is available in green, blue, red, beige, and rust.

40-0626-3 GREEN

The reproduction wallpaper used in Mr. Everard's chamber at the Brush-Everard House is based on fragments of eighteenth-century paper found under cornice molding in the room.

NEW WALLPAPER COLLECTION

These sample swatches are from a new collection of informal country prints by F. Schumacher & Co. that will be available in autumn, 1989. Many of these new wallpapers will coordinate with fabrics from the Abby Aldrich Rockefeller Folk Art Center. Others are reintroductions of favorite *Williamsburg*® wallpaper designs from the eighteenth century. Each of these new interpretive wallpapers will be available in a variety of colors. Clockwise from the top left, they are:

Indian Chintz
Stencil Flowers
Diamond Floral Border (uncut in
    photograph)
Winterberry
Privet Leaves
Tavern Check
Tavern Border (uncut in photograph)
Brunswick
Hopewell
Princess Ann
Field Stripe

BORDERS

Wallpaper borders make an engaging accent in any room, working with painted walls or with other wallpapers. Each of these borders is available in four or five colorways in addition to the mint and beige tones shown here. They also are shown on pages 186 through 191. Clockwise from the top left, the borders shown here are:

Mistletoe Border
Shell Border
Floral Border
Arbor Border
Williamsburg Check Border
Star Border

Palace Ballroom Ceiling White
W61-0410 Flat
W71-0410 Satin

Blair House Buff
W63-1153 Flat
W73-1153 Satin

Palace Chambers Yellow
W62-0405 Flat
W72-0405 Satin

Palace Parlor Cream
W61-0345 Flat
W71-0345 Satin

Daphne Room Beige
W62-1161 Flat
W72-1161 Satin

Brown House Beige
W62-1157 Flat
W73-1157 Satin

James Geddy Tan
W63-1164 Flat
W73-1164 Satin

Palace Supper Room Pale Yellow
W61-0390 Flat
W71-0390 Satin

King's Arms Rose Pink
W61-1027 Flat
W71-1027 Satin

Bassett Hall Green
W62-1152 Flat
W72-1152 Satin

Red Lion Inn Gray
W62-1171 Flat
W72-1171 Satin

Benjamin Powell House Gold
W75-930 Satin Latex

Wetherburn's Tavern Bisque
W61-1172 Flat
W71-1172 Satin

Raleigh Tavern Peach
W61-1047 Flat
W72-1047 Satin

Coachhouse Green
W63-1160 Flat
W73-1160 Satin

Chiswell Gray
W62-0470 Flat
W72-0470 Satin

Palace Supper Room Brown
W76-0205 Satin Latex

Blue Bell Tavern Buff
W62-1154 Flat
W72-1154 Satin

Brick House Light Peach
W61-1156 Flat
W72-1156 Satin

Red Lion Inn Green
W63-1170 Flat
W74-1170 Satin

Pelham Gray
W63-1039 Flat
W73-1039 Satin

Palmer House Brown
W76-942 Satin Latex

Wythe House Gold
W63-1055 Flat
W74-1055 Satin

Raleigh Tavern Tan
W61-1051 Flat
W72-1051 Satin

Prentis Store Gray Green
W64-1168 Flat
W74-1168 Satin

Purdie House Gray
W64-1169 Flat
W74-1169 Satin

Campbell's Tavern Charcoal Brown
W75-931 Satin Latex

Scrivener Store Gold
W62-0420 Flat
W72-0420 Satin

Chowning's Tavern Rose Tan
W63-1019 Flat
W73-1019 Satin

Peyton Randolph Gray
W63-1167 Flat
W73-1167 Satin

Russell House Green
W62-0540 Flat
W72-0540 Satin

Palace Dining Room Pearl Blue
W61-0710 Flat
W71-0710 Satin

Brush-Everard Blue
W64-1158 Flat
W74-1158 Satin

Palace Chambers Green
W63-0560 Flat
W73-0560 Satin

Palace Study Blue
W62-0705 Flat
W72-0705 Satin

Brafferton Blue
W64-1155 Flat
W74-1155 Satin

Market Square Green
W63-1031 Flat
W74-1031 Satin

Wetherburn's Pale Blue
W62-1174 Flat
W72-1174 Satin

Benjamin Powell House Red
W76-935 Satin Latex

Raleigh Tavern Green
W64-1043 Flat
W74-1043 Satin

Apollo Room Blue
W62-1011 Flat Satin
W72-1011 Satin

Raleigh Tavern Chinese Red
W941 Satin Latex (Package Color)

Apothecary Shop Blue
W63-1015 Flat
W73-1015 Satin

James Geddy Gray
W62-1163 Flat
W72-1163 Satin

The painted
background on
these pages is
Williamsburg
Simulated Whitewash
W970 Alkyd Flat
(Package Color)

Robert Nicolson House Green
W63-0555 Flat
W73-0555 Satin

James Southall Blue
W63-1173 Flat
W73-1173 Satin

P A I N T S

IN THE EIGHTEENTH CENTURY

Paint pigments, usually dry, to be mixed with oil and thinner by the painter, were one of the most frequently imported items in eighteenth-century Williamsburg. Paint pigments were also imported "ground in oil" and occasionally ready mixed, as noted in eighteenth-century invoices. Colors included white lead, Prussian blue, ocher, Spanish brown, verdigris, lamp black, indigo, and others.

Early in the eighteenth century, interior woodwork tended to be painted one color, often gray. During the second half of the century, more than one color began to be used. Colors became brighter and doors and baseboards were accented. As evidenced by the St. George Tucker paint specification agreement of 1798, exterior trim was also accented and roofs were painted red. This more lively use of color was perhaps initiated by the increasing affluence of the Virginia colony and the desire to adopt newer fashions.

During the early days of the Williamsburg Restoration, it was determined that paint colors should accurately reflect those used in the eighteenth century. Susan Higginson Nash, an interior designer from Boston, was assigned the task of identifying original colors. Mrs. Nash made several tours of historic houses in Virginia and found that many of the structures still retained their original paint films. She was accompanied by a colorist who used oil paint to match the colors they found.

Where no exposed original paint could be found, the painters used a scalpel or solvents to expose each successive layer of paint and thus determine the prime and finish coats. Colonial Williamsburg was the first historic museum to attempt to replicate period paint colors on such a large scale. The colors in this palette faithfully reproduce those found as they appeared after two hundred years.

— NICHOLAS A. PAPPAS

Nicholas A. Pappas *is the foundation architect for Colonial Williamsburg, with responsibility for ensuring the accuracy of architecture and landscaping in the Historic Area. A Fellow of the American Institute of Architects, Mr. Pappas is an authority on the restoration and rehabilitation of old buildings. He has written, lectured, and taught on many aspects of preservation.*

CARTER'S GROVE, IVORY

EIGHTEENTH – CENTURY
CARPETS

This Caucasian "dragon" Kuba carpet is part of Colonial Williamsburg's extensive study collection of eighteenth-century carpets. Conservation concerns dictate that they not be displayed year-round, but they may be seen at various times in the Historic Area and in the Wallace Gallery.

Floor carpets were treasured objects in the past. They were so rare in the seventeenth and early eighteenth century that the few people who could afford them displayed them on tables, rather than on the floor. By the middle of the eighteenth century, floor coverings became more common and were available in many types and patterns, ranging from locally produced painted canvas and home-made carpeting to expensive imports. Although Oriental carpets were gradually superseded by the products of European looms, some people continued to desire them for their prestige, beauty, and durability.

— LINDA R. BAUMGARTEN
Curator of Textiles

CARTER'S GROVE™ RUG

The Carter's Grove mansion in tidewater Virginia was completed by Carter Burwell in 1755. Built on land purchased early in the eighteenth century by Burwell's grandfather, Robert "King" Carter, the plantation was home to one of the wealthiest and most influential families in Virginia. Mr. and Mrs. Archibald McCrea purchased the mansion in the 1920s and transformed it into a Colonial Revival showpiece. This adaptation carpet is based on the original, which adorned the entrance hall at Carter's Grove when the McCreas lived there. The Persian Herati latticework pattern features rosettes, blossoms, and curved serrated leaves on a network of stems and vines. Available in the original deep navy field as well as deep ivory.

Carter's Grove™ Rug
Ivory 556; Blue 554

    8′3″ × 11′7″
    5′8″ × 8′11″
    4′3″ × 5′9″

CARTER'S GROVE, BLUE

USHAK RUNNER

USHAK CARPET AND HALL RUNNER

Turkey carpets were in demand in Europe from the sixteenth century onward. The name is derived from a town in the middle of the important carpet-weaving district of the Anatolian uplands, east of Smyrna. This carpet features typically Ushak starforms, as well as cloudbands and rosettes. Both the carpet and the hall runner are woven of skein-dyed worsted yarns in the original colors of gold, brick, red and deep blue.

Ushak carpet 552
8′3″ × 11′7″
5′8″ × 8′11″
Ushak hall runner 552
2′6″ × 12′

CARTER'S GROVE™ HALL RUNNER

This hall runner is adapted from the Persian Herati pattern in the carpet that graced the entrance hall of Carter's Grove mansion in Virginia in the twentieth century. It features stylized leaves, rosettes, and a framework of stems and vines. This 100 percent wool adaptation offers a handsome and durable foundation on which to build a traditional feeling.

Carter's Grove™ Hall Runner, Blue 554
2′6″ × 12′

CARTER'S GROVE RUNNER

TURKISH CHURCH

TURKISH CHURCH CARPET

In this adaptation of an unusual seventeenth- or eighteenth-century Transylvania prayer rug, lamps or vases hang in the niches at both ends of the field while rosettes adorn the spandrels. The palmettes, border cartouches, and reciprocal guards are more typical of this period. This pattern was named after the large number of such rugs found in churches in the Transylvania region of Romania, a major distribution center for these carpets while it was under Turkish rule in the seventeenth and eighteenth centuries.

Turkish Church Carpet 553
    3′10″ × 5′3″
    5′7″ × 8′8″
    8′2″ × 11′9″

CHECKED CARPET

This flat-woven carpet is adapted from a nineteenth-century American carpet fragment made of cotton. Weavers of this period were skilled craftsmen who provided carpets and coverlets. A carpet such as this checked design was usually woven yardage of widths sewn together to cover most of the floor in a room. In the eighteenth and nineteenth centuries, "carpet" generally referred to a floor covering while "rug" referred to a bed covering.

4′ × 6′; 6′ × 9′
Other sizes available by inquiry.

TALCOTT CARPET

This colorful, flat-woven carpet is adapted in several color ways from a hand-loomed, hand-dyed design shown in a nineteenth-century painting. In 1832, three generations of the Talcott family of upstate New York posed for an untutored artist named Deborah Goldsmith. Using watercolors, pencil, and gold paint on paper, the artist carefully captured the decorative details of the scene. Today, her painting is valued for its charm and for its view of period clothing and furniture.

Abigail, Betsey, and Charles available in 27″ widths in any length up to 25′. Betsey also available in 3′ × 5′ and 6′ × 9′ sizes.

CHECKED

BETSEY TALCOTT

CHARLES TALCOTT

ABIGAIL TALCOTT

LIGHTING
IN THE EIGHTEENTH CENTURY

In colonial Virginia candles were the primary source of artificial light among those who have left written records. While these people were mainly the upper classes, they were little better off than their less affluent contemporaries in terms of the lighting technology available to them. They might have been able to afford a greater number of candles that burned more efficiently and smoked less, but candles could only provide so much light regardless of how wealthy a person might be. For everyone, the hours after sunset were ones of dark and shadow.

Eighteenth-century candles were made of myrtle wax, beeswax, tallow, or spermaceti. They were either dipped or molded around a cotton wick that had been spun for the purpose (plaited wicks were not used until the following century). These wicks were not self-consuming and had to be trimmed constantly with snuffers to keep the candle burning efficiently. Fire was a constant hazard from the open flame of both candles and fireplaces, the latter also being an important light source at least during winter.

This set of four silver candlesticks was made in 1745/46 by Paul deLamerie, a member of the Huguenot community in London. These displaced French Protestants, largely artisans, contributed immeasurably to the sophistication of English design in the seventeenth and eighteenth centuries. In the form of Ionic columns, these sticks are the only known examples from the first half of the century to exhibit architectural correctness.

The silver candlestick made by Boston silversmith Edward Winslow between 1715 and 1725 shows how quickly fashions in decorative accessories spread to the colonies. Its baluster shape and faceted surfaces parallel late baroque designs made in London at the same time.

This 1768 mezzotint engraving of "A Philosopher Giving a Lecture in which a Lamp Is Put in the Place of the Sun" shows the harsh contrast between lamp or candlelight and dark corners that would have been so familiar to our ancestors.

The three glass lusters that Lord Botetourt purchased for the ballroom at the Palace provided impressive illumination, both for the paintings of the king and queen and for the dancers beneath them.

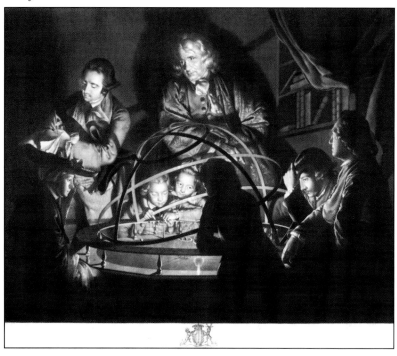

Many types of candlesticks were available for a wide variety of uses. The most common sort of candlestick was a columnar or baluster type made of metal, ceramic, or glass. More specialized was the chamberstick, which had a saucerlike base that prevented wax from dripping while the stick was carried. In public buildings chandeliers or lusters, the latter made of glass, might be used. For outdoor lighting a lantern, with its sides enclosed either by glass or pierced metal, protected the candle's flame from the wind and inclement weather.

During the day candles and sticks were stored in central locations within the dwelling for easy access at sunset. Period graphics suggest that those who did not follow this practice were slack in their household management. Thus, candles seldom appear in period paintings and prints in daylight scenes, unless needed for a specific purpose such as melting wax for sealing letters.

— BETTY C. LEVINER

By the rococo period many lighting devices, both silver and ceramic, had become as much ornamental as functional. This whimsical pair of porcelain sticks is from the Chelsea factory.

Although the wealthy could indulge in ornamental forms of lighting, there was still widespread demand for utilitarian lighting devices such as this "hogscraper" candlestick of sheet iron and brass.

Betty C. Leviner is curator of exhibition buildings. Her research in primary documents, especially diaries and inventories, contributes to the accurate interpretation of the houses in the Historic Area. She has written a forthcoming book on the pictorial and documentary sources used in furnishing the exhibition buildings.

CW12939

CW12895

CW12894

CW12891

CW12596

CHANDELIER

In the eighteenth century, light was a precious commodity. Chandeliers, perhaps the most lavish display of lighting, were reserved for the well-to-do of the period. This handsome brass candle or electrified chandelier with its intricately worked chain is inspired by an original that formerly hung in the governor's office at Colonial Williamsburg. It features eight arms and two indirect lights in the base. It is available in polished or antiqued brass. Height 40"; Diameter 32"; Total length 52" with 12" suspension chain. CW12939

CHANDELIER

In the eighteenth century, the Raleigh Tavern was the scene of public receptions, balls, and banquets. Here George Washington talked politics with Patrick Henry, the Phi Beta Kappa Society was formed, and land, slaves, and goods were sold. This chandelier, which formerly hung in the Raleigh Tavern, is available with four lights, as in the original, and also with five or six lights in polished or antiqued brass or pewter for use with candles or electricity. Height 18½"; Diameter 23"; Total length 37" with two 17" suspension links. CW12895

CHANDELIER

This graceful candle or electric chandelier is available with six lights, as in the original, or with five lights in polished or antiqued brass. Height 18"; Diameter 19"; Total length 38" with 20" suspension chain. CW12894

CHANDELIER

Completed in 1722, the residence of Virginia's royal governor was considered one of the most grand buildings in the British colonies of North America. The building's furnishings reflected the elegance of its architecture. This chandelier, which formerly hung in the Palace, features a drop pendant and four (as in the original), five, or eight lights in polished or antiqued pewter. It is available for candles or electricity. Height 20"; Diameter 28¼"; Total length 40" with 20" suspension chain. CW12891

CAPITOL CHANDELIER

Reproduced from an original made in Holland circa 1690-1730, a two-tier chandelier such as this may have lighted discussions of Ben Franklin's recently published *Poor Richard's Almanack* or William Parks's new *Virginia Gazette*. This chandelier features handsome S-scroll arms with tips shaped to imply animal heads, with large dots for eyes. It has twelve arms and is available for candles or electricity in polished or antiqued brass. Height 24"; Diameter 26"; Total length 40" with 16" suspension chain. CW12596

Lord Botetourt had three expensive cut glass lusters made in London for the ballroom of the Governor's Palace. They illuminated his portraits of King George III and Queen Charlotte and must have been dazzling to Virginians invited to dance there.

CW 12579

CW 12580

PRINTING OFFICE CHANDELIER

In 1639 in Cambridge, Massachusetts, the first North American printing press began operating, fueling the spread of information in the colonies. The six-light American original of this reproduction was made in the last decades of the eighteenth century. The tinsmith crafted the double cone center, turned edge arms, fluted cups, and wire links on tin-coated sheet iron. It is available with four, five, or six arms in antiqued tin or black painted tin and in candle and electric versions. Height 15"; Diameter 26½"; Total length 45" with four suspension links. CW 12579

TIN CHANDELIER

British colonists brought tinwork to the New World. The original of this neoclassic six-light design was made in America in the late 1700s or early 1800s. Fluted candle saucers made for easier removal of wax. It is available for candles or electricity in antiqued tin or painted black. Height 27"; Diameter 24"; Height with canopy 41½" with 12" suspension chain. CW 12580

CHANDELIER

A chandelier similar to this may have illuminated spirited discussions among George Washington, Thomas Jefferson, Patrick Henry, and other burgesses after Governor Botetourt dissolved the Virginia General Assembly following protests against the British Revenue Act. It is available in antiqued or black painted tin candles or electrified with four, five, six, or eight lights. Height 11½"; Diameter 27"; Total length 39½" with four suspension links. CW 12578

CAMPBELL'S TAVERN CHANDELIER

The original of this graceful, informal, two-tiered iron, tin, and turned wood chandelier was made in New England about 1785, the same year that Thomas Jefferson introduced his Statute for Religious Freedom designed to abolish the practice of religious tests in Virginia. There is also a one-tiered adaptation. Available for candles or electricity. Height 26"; Diameter 30"; Total length 38" with 12" suspension chain. CW 12600 shown

CW12578

CW12600

Lanterns were frequently used in passages; here the candle-light shining through the pierced tin creates a play of pattern on the ceiling.

CW 12700

CAMPBELL'S TAVERN LANTERN

The original of this tin, glass, and maple six-sided lantern was made in New England. There is a circular opening in the center of the base for easy removal and adjustment of the tin candle holder. Also available for electricity. Height 14½"; Diameter 8¾"; Length 6⅝" with 16" suspension chain. CW 12700

GAOLER'S LANTERN

Lanterns of this type were very popular in the eighteenth century. Reproductions are available in antiqued tin finish. Hand lantern, candle only: 5½" × 5½"; Height 14". CW 12800

Wall lantern, electric only: 5½" × 5½"; Height 14", for indoor use only. CW 12801

CW 12800

WEST CARRIAGE GATE LANTERN

Handsomely crowned and finished in copper or copper finished black, this adaptation of an eighteenth-century outdoor lantern makes a bold statement. Height 22½"; Width 11"; Depth 9½", electric only. CW 12879

EAST CARRIAGE GATE LANTERN

Topped with a refined dentil design, this adaptation of an eighteenth-century outdoor lantern is available in polished copper or copper finished black. Height 17¾"; Width 11⅜"; Depth 7", electric only. CW 12877

CW 12879

CW 12877

TAYLOE HOUSE LANTERN

The filigreed base adds interest to this simple, elegant bell design. It is available in both verdigris brass and polished brass for candle or three electric lights. Height 23″; Diameter 10″; Total length 39″ with 16″ suspension chain. CW 11758

GOVERNOR'S PALACE LANTERN

This hexagonal brass and glass lantern is decorated with cast fleurs-de-lis and vase-shaped feet. The English original, circa 1750-1790, held a candle made of tallow, bayberry, myrtlewax, beeswax, spermaceti, or stearin. A smaller 4-light adaptation and 6-light electric version also are available. Not shown but available is large size for 1 candle. Height 34″; Width across corners 18″; Total length 46″ with 12″ suspension chain. CW 12892

CW 11758

CW 12892

CW 12880

LANTERN

This timeless eighteenth-century design often is emulated in contemporary lighting designs. Handsomely cast arms add interest. Polished and antiqued brass are available either for candle or three electric lights. Height 23″; Diameter 12″; Total length 39″ with 16″ suspension chain. CW 12880

GOVERNOR'S PALACE HALL LANTERN

This brass lantern's formality is softened by curved, loosely scrolled supports, cast leaf decoration, and delicately turned feet. It is available in polished brass with beveled glass panels for candle or 4-light electric. Height 32″; Width 12½″; Depth 9¼″; Total length 44″ with 12″ suspension chain. CW 12893

BRUSH-EVERARD LANTERN

Reproduced from a circa 1750 English original, this 4-light lantern features delicate C-scroll supports, scalloped side panels, and scroll-and-shell feet. There also is a smaller 3-light version. Available in polished or antiqued brass for candle or electricity. Height 23″; Width 10½″; Height 39″ with 16″ suspension chain. Candle in large size only. CW 11751

CW 12893

CW 11751

CW 16-74E

CW 16-23

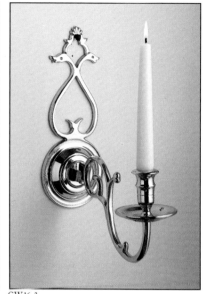

CW 16-3

HOUSE OF BURGESSES SCONCE

A reproduction of this twin sconce is available in polished brass on walnut, with an adaptation in antiqued brass. Available for candles or electricity. Backplate height 6¼″; Backplate width 3¼″; Arm depth 7″.
CW 16-74E

PALACE SAUCERBACK SCONCE

Softly reflected light characterizes this simple reproduction American antiqued tin saucer design made about 1780-1830. Candle only. Height 10¾″; Diameter 9¾″; Depth 5½″. CW 13160

DOUBLE ARM SCONCE

Made in England circa 1770, the original of this design features S-scroll arms and graceful globes. This reproduction is available in polished or antiqued brass. Candle only. Height with globes 17″; Width 15½″; Backplate diameter 3⁵⁄₁₆″; Depth 9″.
CW 16-23

PALACE CRIMPED EDGE SCONCE

This reproduction of an American tinned sheet-iron sconce, circa 1780-1830, features a broad plate to reflect light and ribbing to refract it. It is available in antiqued tin. Height 13½″; Diameter 11½″; Depth 5¼″. Candle only. CW 13159

PALACE WARMING ROOM SCONCE

Made of polished or antiqued brass, this intricately formed sconce features a handsomely S-curved arm and broad plate for catching errant wax. Available for candle or electricity. Backplate height 10½″; Backplate width 4⅛″; Arm depth 10⅝″. CW 16-3

SERVANTS' QUARTERS AND WYTHE HOUSE KITCHEN SCONCES

Diminutive sconces made of tin feature crimping for diffused illumination. Servants' Quarters: Height 10″; Width 4½″; Depth 4¾″. Candle and electricity. CW 13162
Wythe House: Height 8½″; Width 2½″; Depth 2¾″. Candle only. CW 13161

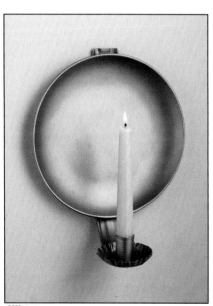

CW 13160

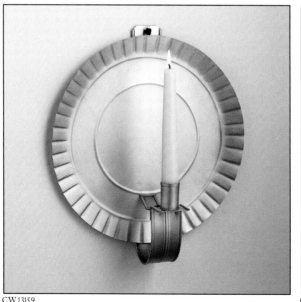

CW 13159

CW 13162   CW 13161

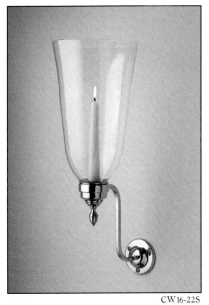

CW 16-22S

CW 16-22D

CW 130

BRUTON HURRICANE SCONCE

Polished brass highlights the S-curved arm, drop pendant, and handmade crystal globe. Available for candle or electricity. Height 17″ with 10″ globe, 20″ with 13″ globe; Backplate diameter 3¾″; Arm depth 12″. CW 16-22S

PRINTING OFFICE SCONCE

Reproduced from an American original circa 1780-1820, the crimped edge and S-curved arm are typical of the period. Available in antiqued tin, candle only. Height 13″; Width 3⅞″ bottom, 5⅛″ top; Depth 6″. CW 13163

DOUBLE ARM BRUTON HURRICANE SCONCE

Candlemaking was messy and time-consuming but, since candles were the primary source of artificial light through the early nineteenth century, it was an essential task. Adapted from the single-arm Bruton design, this simple but elegant sconce in polished brass features 10″ or 13″ handmade crystal globes for candles or electricity. Total height 17″ with 10″ globe, 20″ with 13″ globe: Width 16″; Depth 9″. CW 16-22D

PALACE KITCHEN SCONCE

Adapted from an English or American brass and copper original, circa 1780-1830, this antiqued tin sconce features an attractively crimped and folded surface to create many reflective facets. Candle only. Height 12″; Diameter 10″; Depth 4½″. CW 13158

WALL SCONCE WITH MIRROR

This reproduction of an eighteenth-century English antique features dark mahogany cut, assembled, and finished by hand to duplicate the cabinetwork of the original. The protective glass slides up for easy access to a candlestick. Height 18″; Width 13⅜″; Depth 6½″. CW 130

WALL LANTERN

This fine reproduction wall lantern features solid, select mahogany as found in the eighteenth-century English original. The meticulous cabinetry accompanied by glass frames with double molded edges indicate the quality of detail, scale, and construction given to wood accessories during this period. Height 16¼″; Width 6¼″; Depth 6¼″. CW 16-81

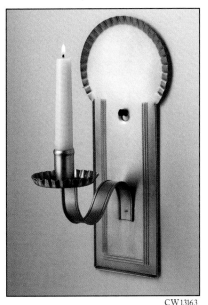

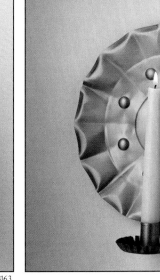

CW 13163

CW 13158

CW 16-81

DELFT TOBACCO JAR LAMP

DELFT STORAGE JAR LAMP

DELFT TOBACCO JAR LAMP

During the seventeenth and eighteenth centuries, tobacco was known as "the bewitching vegetable," an American cash crop whose usage became very popular in both England and the colonies. In Williamsburg, store-keepers may have kept their patrons' favorite tobacco blends in delft tobacco jars such as the one reproduced for the base of this interpretive lamp. It features the name "Carolina," like the original, and is one of a series dedicated to states known to have grown or exported tobacco during this period. Height 27½".

DELFT STORAGE JAR LAMP

Colorful, affordable, and highly decorative delft was very popular in both England and the colonies during the eighteenth century. This impressive interpretive lamp is based on a whimsically decorated antique vase made about 1700 in Bristol, England. The lamp base is a reproduction of this vase and features three different scenes. Height 27¾".

BALUSTER CANDLESTICK LAMP

Baluster candlesticks were developed in England in the 1680s and featured an inverted baluster or vase form on the main part of the stem. The base of this interpretation of an eighteenth-century lighting source is reproduced by expert craftsmen using a sand-casting technique similar to the process used to make the original. The brass in this lamp is whiter and brighter than most modern metal, duplicating the color and patina of the original. Height 14". CW 16-20E

SMALL SPIKE CANDLESTICK LAMP

"Pricket sticks" were a seventeenth-century invention designed to spear candles to keep them upright. This interpretive lamp is based on just such a candlestick design. The master pattern is used to shape a sand mold for the base into which molten brass is poured. The reproduction casting is carefully trimmed, ground, and polished by hand. Height 12". CW 16-32E

CW 16-20E, CW 16-32E

MID-DRIP CANDLESTICK LAMP

During the seventeenth century, candles were made of animal fat or beeswax subject to considerable dripping and sputtering. The "mid-drip" design was intended to catch such a candle's residue. The candlestick base of this interpretive lamp is reproduced from an antique made in Europe about 1680 using similar sand-casting, brazing, and pinning techniques. Height 18½". CW16-12E

TALL CANDLESTICK LAMP

Brass often has been an imitative metal, taking its designs from more costly silver. It also has been used as a substitute for gold by the use of coloring agents in the lacquer finish to heighten the resemblance. The base of this interpretive lamp is reproduced in brass from an unusually tall eighteenth-century Continental candlestick. Height 27½". CW16-34E

GOVERNOR'S PALACE CANDLESTICK LAMP

During the eighteenth century, candles were the primary method of lighting dark rooms during the evening. Only people of means could afford the luxury of using many candlesticks or candelabra. The cast brass of this interpretive lamp is reproduced from an antique believed to be French in origin.
Height 21½". CW16-36E

SPIKE CANDLESTICK LAMP

By the time Williamsburg was settled, spike candlesticks or "pricket sticks" designed during the seventeenth century were being phased out as craftsmen began producing more convenient nozzled

Left to right: CW16-12E, CW16-34E, CW16-36E

candlesticks. The reproduction base of this interpretive lamp is made using sand-casting, trimming, grinding, and polishing techniques similar to the eighteenth-century original.
Height 20½". CW16-33E

BRUSH-EVERARD CANDLESTICK LAMP

Prior to creating the trumpet shaped candlestick in the mid-sixteenth century, most English brass makers copied candlesticks of Continental design. This modern interpretation of a seventeenth-century lighting source features a solid brass "trumpet" base embellished with bold sausage turning.
Height 21½". CW16-13E

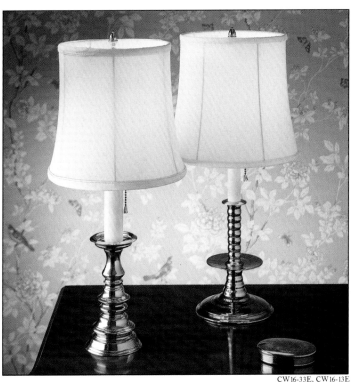

CW16-33E, CW16-13E

The dramatic lighting in this scene suggests that candles were precious. The tutor to the children of Councillor Robert Carter, one of the richest men in pre-revolutionary Virginia, was impressed when seven candles lit the Carters' dining room, calling it a "brilliant display."

CW 16-39C   CW 8

BRASS TAPERSTICK

Tapersticks were introduced around 1680 as a writing table accoutrement used for melting sealing wax. This brass reproduction, based on a late seventeenth-century English original, features a wide drip-pan midway down the stem to protect tabletops from hot wax. It can be used with a 9″ lead crystal hurricane shade. Height 4″.
Taperstick CW 16-39C.
9″ Hurricane shade CW 8.

CANDLESTICK WITH GLOBE

Like the eighteenth-century original, this reproduction candlestick is made of hand-turned mahogany, mouth-blown lead crystal, and polished brass. Globes such as this allowed molded or dipped candles to burn more evenly and protected them from drafts. Height 16¼″. CW 16-80

CW 16-80

BALUSTER CANDLESTICK

While only the well-to-do in eighteenth-century England and America could afford silver candlesticks, brass was far more practical for most people. An inventory taken in 1771 after the death of Raleigh Tavern keeper Anthony Hay lists twenty-four brass candlesticks among the tavern's furnishings. Employing the same sand-casting technique used to make the original, this reproduction of an eighteenth-century brass English antique derives its name from the shape of its stem. Baluster candlesticks feature a baluster or vase form for the main part of the stem, a design that was developed in England in the 1680s and remained popular throughout the eighteenth century. It can be used alone or with a 14″ leaded crystal shade. Height 5¾″.
Candlestick CW 16-20.
14″ Hurricane shade CW9.

CW 16-20   CW 9

ROUND BASE CANDLESTICK

Reproduced from an eighteenth-century antique, this graceful candlestick is sand-cast the same way as the original. Specially formulated molten alloy designed to duplicate the color and patina of eighteenth-century brass is poured into sand molds made of the original piece. Temperature, moisture, and general atmospheric conditions all affect this ancient form of craftsmanship. Shrinkage occurs as the molten metal cools, requiring a pattern that is larger but still duplicates each detail of the original. Only about 60 percent of cast candlesticks achieve high enough quality for finishing. Tiny pits and blemishes on the polished surfaces are characteristic of the sand-casting process. In this reproduction, a special lacquer closes the pores and makes the metal tarnish resistant. It can be used with an 18″ leaded glass shade. Height 8″.
Candlestick CW 16-2.
18″ Hurricane shade CW 10.

CW 16-2   CW 10

CANDLEHOLDER

This reproduction of an eighteenth-century antique can be used on the wall or tabletop. The base, socket, and handle are made separately, then joined and finished by hand. Height 6½". CW 16-38

HAND CANDLESTICK WITH EXTINGUISHER

Reproduced from an English antique, this hand-carried sand-cast candlestick provided light in dark staircases and hallways. The wide dish also caught dripping animal fats, beeswax, bayberry wax, and spermaceti, which burned faster than their wicking, a problem solved in the following century by adding a tight thread to the plaited wick to hold it close to the edge of the flame. Diameter 6". CW 16-73

RALEIGH TAVERN CHAMBERSTICK

Reproduced from an English original circa 1750, this brass chamberstick was a popular household design. Plain, practical, and well balanced in the hand, it offered a portable source of light en route to the bedchamber. Height 2½"; Length, including handle 8½". CW 16-21

PEWTER CHAMBERSTICK

This reproduction of an English chamberstick exemplifies the features most desirable in an eighteenth-century night light. The fat finger ring makes it easy to carry while the wide saucer-shaped base catches dripping fat or hot wax. Height 3¼"; Diameter 5¾". CW 87

Clockwise from top: CW 16-38, CW 16-73, CW 16-21, CW 87

C 57 C 38

CANDLESTICK

This unusual octagonal delft-ware candlestick is repro-duced from a Liverpool, England, original circa 1750. Its white opaque surface is derived from adding tin ashes to lead silica compound. Height 7". C 57

CANDLESTICK

Reproduced from a Liverpool, England, delftware original circa 1750, this candleholder was used in a food warmer. Tin-enameled earthenware was extremely popular in eigh-teenth-century Williamsburg. Height 2½". C 38

TRAVELING CANDLEHOLDERS

Eighteenth-century ingenuity manifests iself in this repro-duction of an English antique circa 1770. The halves unscrew to form a pair of sturdy candle bases. Two can-dle sockets are stored inside and threaded for easy attachment. Diameter 3¾"; Height 2½". CW 16-37

CW 16-33

CW 16-32

SPIKE CANDLESTICKS

Also known as a "pricket stick," this reproduction of a European seventeenth-century antique speared the candle base to hold it in place. This design persisted into the eighteenth century, when it was replaced by a socket or nozzle. The smaller size is an adaptation. Taller candlestick height 7½". CW 16-33. Height 4". CW 16-32

MID-DRIP CANDLESTICK

The tray on the stem of this late seventeenth-century candlestick was designed to catch wax guttering down the sides of candles. While an improvement over the previous suet candles, drip pans were still required. This candlestick is reproduced from a European antique circa 1680. Height 8½". CW 16-12

BRUSH-EVERARD CANDLESTICK

Reproduced from an early seventeenth-century "trumpet" candlestick embellished with bold sausage turning, this piece illustrates a purely English design. Prior to this, English brass candlesticks were copied from French and Low Countries designs. Height 8". CW 16-13

SWIRL BASE CANDLESTICK

The handsome swirling design made in England about 1765 distinguishes this sand-cast brass candlestick. The mold for the reproduction was made directly from the original. Castings are made one at a time, then filed and polished by hand. Height 8½". CW 16-10

CW 16-12

CW 16-13

CW 16-10

Left to right: CW16-35, CW16-34, CW16-36

Inventories indicate that candlesticks were stored in closets and then brought out at dark, rather than displayed on mantels and tables during the day when not in use.

CW 16-5

OCTAGONAL BASE CANDLESTICK

This solid brass candlestick is reproduced from an eighteenth-century Dutch antique. Its octagonal base and carefully proportioned stem are derived from similar shapes worked in silver during this period. This is not surprising considering the prohibitive cost of silver candlesticks for all but the well-to-do in America and in Europe. Height 7". CW 16-35

TALL CANDLESTICK

Reproduced from an eighteenth-century Continental design complete with drip-tray, this candlestick is sand-cast using the same methods as in the original. Height 12½". CW 16-34

GOVERNOR'S PALACE CANDLESTICK

This design is reproduced from an eighteenth-century candlestick believed to be French in origin. Until well into the seventeenth century, most English candlesticks were derived from designs developed in France and the Low Countries. Height 9". CW 16-36

SQUARE BASE CANDLESTICK

The sturdy original of this reproduction cast brass candlestick was made in the late baroque style circa 1720. It features a symmetrical base and rigid ball feet. Height 6¾". CW 16-5

SCISSORS CANDLESNUFFER AND CANDLE EXTINGUISHER

Reproduced from an English original circa 1720-1735, this scissors snuffer was used to trim wicks that caused candles to gutter. The box on the blade caught the charred wick end to keep it from falling against the burning candle. The reproduction of an eighteenth-century candle extinguisher features a long handle and swinging brass cone ideal for putting out candles in sconces, chandeliers, and hurricane shades. It could be hung by the hole in the handle when not in use. Scissors Candlesnuffer CW 16-18. Candle Extinguisher CW 16-27.

CW 16-18

CW 16-27

223

CW 16-65

CW 16-45

Candlelight glistens off a gilded looking glass in the upper middle room of the Governor's Palace.

PALACE BALLROOM CANDELABRA

This sand-cast reproduction of an early eighteenth-century English antique is impressive in scale. Until 1769, eight such candelabra were the principal means of lighting the Governor's Palace Ballroom. Lord Botetourt later added three glass chandeliers, or "lusters," to brighten the room. Height 19¼"; Width 18¼". CW 16-65

GOVERNOR'S PALACE BALLROOM CANDLESTICK

This adaptation of an eighteenth-century English brass candelabrum is larger than most candlesticks of the period. It also features brighter, whiter brass than most modern metal, but closer in color and patina to that used by eighteenth-century craftsmen. Height 15¾". CW 16-45

CANDELABRA

This candelabra is reproduced from a double-armed eighteenth-century antique. It was convenient for use on a harpsichord or spinet, or on a desk in a library. This sand-cast candelabra features arms that move up and down as well as to the right and left. Height 16". CW 16-63

TRUMPET BASE CANDLESTICK

This reproduction of a mid-eighteenth-century candlestick features the trumpet-shaped base introduced by English metalsmiths, both in silver and brass, a century earlier. It lacks the drip pan of early English examples. Height 8¼". CW 16-24

CANDLESTICK

The original of this pewter candlestick was made in England about 1710-1720. Like the original, it is made by casting molten alloy into molds, then carefully polishing and burnishing the rough surfaces to bring up the luster of the metal. Height 7¼". CW 30

CW 16-63

CW 16-24

CW 30

Left to right: APRIL, JUNE, OCTOBER, DECEMBER

P R I N T S
IN THE EIGHTEENTH CENTURY

Elegant and fashionable additions to the home in the eighteenth century, prints were produced in quantities large enough to make them affordable alternative to paintings. Shopkeepers' records, household inventories, and other written sources reveal that prints were widely available in colonial America.

Subject matter varied greatly and filled a number of needs: print sets depicting the months, the seasons, the elements, or the senses were often mentioned; foreign views and historical scenes served an educational purpose; scripture prints illustrated theological stories and moral ideals; portraits of scholars, learned gentlemen, and famous persons — referred to as "heads" — were widely noted. Prints of paintings of old masters (particularly Rembrandt and Rubens), as well as living artists such as Kneller and Reynolds, were an alternative to owning an original. One of the most popular eighteenth-century printmakers, William Hogarth, popularized the print as a medium in its own right. His social and political satires were in great demand throughout England and the colonies.

Advances in the arts and sciences spawned increasing interest in the field of natural history. New efforts to explore and document the natural world produced countless publications such as Mark Catesby's *Natural History of Carolina, Florida and the Bahama Islands*. Enthusiasm for gardening prompted professional gardeners to publish seed catalogs, the most popular being *The Twelve Months of Flowers* by Robert Furber.

Maps were also widely used in America, providing the most up-to-date information on new explorations. They were necessary for navigation, for understanding local geography, while waging war, and in settling boundary disputes. Maps tell modern scholars what people knew about the land at any given time. They record changes in land formation and illustrate the locations of settlements that have been lost over time.

Prints and maps could be seen and purchased in colonial stores, and print and book sellers' shops. Individuals ordered specific items from London agents or had them shipped to the colonies. The popularity and availability of prints and maps facilitated the spread of knowledge, fashion, and cultural ideals in the eighteenth century. These reproductions from the Colonial Williamsburg collections reflect the beliefs and tastes of early Americans.

— MARGARET B. PRITCHARD

Margaret B. Pritchard, curator of prints and maps, has done extensive research on the Bodleian plate, the engraved copper plate showing the Palace, the college, and the Capitol at Williamsburg. The plate was found at the Bodleian Library at Oxford in the 1920s. Ms. Pritchard is preparing a catalog of the maps in the collection.

FURBER FRUIT PRINTS

These "Twelve Months of Fruits" are reproduced from a set of originals commissioned in 1732 by Robert Furber, an English nurseryman. He selected 364 varieties of fruits, then grouped them according to the months in which his London patrons could expect them to ripen in a garden or greenhouse. He identified each with its botanical name to ensure purchase of the proper seed or plant. These prints met with instant success and were sold out soon after publication. To capture the fine details of the originals, each of these twelve prints has been reproduced on 100% rag paper. They are individually hand-tinted to duplicate the original colors.

Framed   21″ × 24″
Unframed   18½″ × 24″

	Framed	Unframed
January Fruit	24596	25452
February Fruit	24604	25494
March Fruit	24638	25536
April Fruit	24646	25551
May Fruit	24679	25601
June Fruit	24687	25668
July Fruit	24711	25700
August Fruit	24729	25734
September Fruit	24737	25817
October Fruit	24752	25858
November Fruit	24786	25924
December Fruit	24794	25965

JANUARY

FEBRUARY

MARCH

AUGUST

SEPTEMBER

OCTOBER

NOVEMBER

DECEMBER

Sets of prints appealed to the eighteenth-century taste for classification. Robert Furber's seed catalogs, published as sets of a dozen fruit or flower prints, are documented in colonial Virginia inventories, so they are appropriate in the stair passage of the George Wythe House.

FURBER FLORAL PRINTS

In 1730, Robert Furber, a nurseryman in Kensington, England, commissioned London engravers to produce a twelve-page seed catalog featuring arrangements of flowers that bloomed in gardens and greenhouses in England during each month. Furber selected 400 varieties, all of which he offered to his London patrons. Each variety was identified by its proper botanical name. The catalog was sold out soon after publication to people who were interested not only in purchasing seeds and plants, but who also wanted the prints for decoration. Furber's flowers have been reproduced on 100% rag paper to capture the fine detail of the originals, and hand-tinted to duplicate the true colors.

Framed   18″ × 23″
Unframed   16″ × 21″

	Framed	Unframed
January Floral	24943	23929
February Floral	25072	23911
March Floral	25098	23887
April Floral	24851	23861
May Floral	24844	23838
June Floral	24828	23796
July Floral	24810	23770
August Floral	25031	23754
September Floral	25130	23713
October Floral	25171	23689
November Floral	25197	23671
December Floral	25239	23630

Clockwise from top left: APRIL, MAY, JUNE, JULY

EGGPLANT

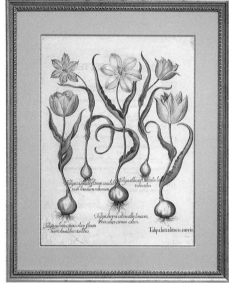

TULIP

IRIS OPEN/IRIS CLOSED

As a result of extensive British exploration and colonization in the seventeenth and eighteenth centuries, botanical enthusiasts began an international exchange of seeds, roots, bulbs, and cuttings in addition to information often shared through detailed illustrations such as these. The originals of these reproductions were engraved in England in 1767 by J. Sowerby for the Lambeth Botanic Gardens.

Framed 12½″ × 15½″
Unframed 11″ × 14″

	Framed	Unframed
Iris Open	28126	24778
Iris Closed	28167	24745

BESLER BOTANICALS

The natural world in general, and botany and agriculture in particular, were of great interest during the seventeenth and eighteenth centuries. Botanical engravings were a means of education as well as a form of decoration. This series of prints has been reproduced from original prints. The Eggplant Botanical and Tulip Botanical prints have been reproduced from the Besler book, *Hortus Eystenttensis*, published in Eichstatt, Germany, in 1613. Five other prints have been reproduced from original prints or copies engraved from 1613 through 1713 and appear to be from two different editions of the book. Framed 21″ × 25½″ Unframed 19″ × 23½″

	Framed	Unframed
Eggplant Botanical	142414	138032
Tulip Botanical	142422	138024
Two Hyacinths	162339	158402
Three Narcissus	162347	158394
Two Muscari and One Hyacinth	162354	158360

AMARYLLIS PRINTS

These prints are adapted from original hand-engravings by T. Jeffreys, published by Philip Miller in June 1755, and included in *Figures of the Most Beautiful, Useful, and Uncommon Plants Described in the Gardener's Dictionary Vol. I and II*, London, 1771. Thomas Jefferson, an enthusiastic gardener, featured this book in his list of 148 titles that should comprise a gentleman's library.

Framed 20½″ × 27½″
Unframed 18½″ × 25½″

	Framed	Unframed
Amaryllis Plate 23	142638	141366
Amaryllis Plate 24	142620	141358

"BELLADONNA AMARYLLIS" AND "KEIZER JOSEPHUS"

These handsome botanical prints are reproduced from Jacob Trew's *Hortus Nitidissimus* published in Nuremburg, Germany, in 1750. The Belladona Amaryllis, reputed to be one of Thomas Jefferson's favorite flowers, was painted by renowned botanical illustrator George Ehret and engraved by Seligman. The Keizer Josephus, probably also painted by Ehret, was engraved by A. L. Wirsing.

Framed 18″ × 23¾″
Unframed 16″ × 21¾″

	Framed	Unframed
Belladonna Amaryllis	172486	165118
Keizer Josephus	172502	165100

TWO HYACINTHS

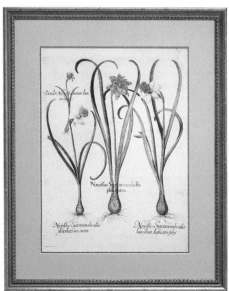

THREE NARCISSUS

TWO MUSCARI AND ONE HYACINTH

Left to right top: AMARYLLIS PLATE 23, CLOSED IRIS, AMARYLLIS PLATE 24   BOTTOM: BELLADONNA, OPEN IRIS, KEIZER JOSEPHUS

"CHERRIES"

"PLUMS"

ALPHABET PRINT

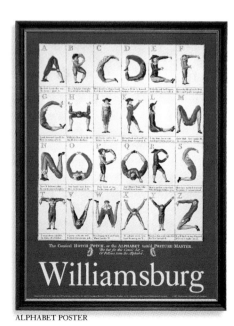

ALPHABET POSTER

"CHERRIES" AND "PLUMS"

These prints are reproduced from among 90 selected plates in the book *Pomona Britannica* published in 1812. This volume depicts fruit grown in and around London, particularly in the gardens at Hampton Court. The engravings were made by George Brookshaw of London in June 1806. They were printed in aquatint and then hand-colored.

Framed   20½″ × 24½″
Unframed   18½″ × 22½″

	Framed	Unframed
Cherries	172494	165126
Plums	172478	165134

"THE ALPHABET TURN'D POSTURE-MASTER"

Published in 1782 in London by Carington Bowles, this reproduction print and poster are based on a hand-tinted print that features cavorting, jovial characters providing an instructive view of the alphabet through posture and rhyme. In accordance with the custom of the period, "J" and "U" are omitted as most people preferred to use "I" and "V" instead.

Poster   Framed   20″ × 26″
             Unframed   18″ × 24″
Print   Framed   18½″ × 13½″
             Unframed   16½″ × 11½″

	Framed	Unframed
Poster	163501	162677
Print	26534	78121

The eighteenth century was the "Age of Enlightenment," when man's exploration and analysis of the natural world flourished. In 1735 Linnaeus published his Systema Naturae, *establishing a binomial classification system for plants and animals. This interest in "natural philosophy," as science was called, is reflected in the shell print on a chair seat in the student's chamber at the Wythe House.*

SHELL PRINTS

In the seventeenth and eighteenth centuries, the interest and curiosity of Englishmen and colonists alike were stimulated by ever-increasing exploration of the world. These lovely prints are reproduced from a meticulously detailed and hand-colored series published by Gabriel Muller in Germany, circa 1755-1758. They represent the efforts of naturalists to record each detail of the flora and fauna around them.

Framed   18″ × 24″
Unframed   16″ × 22″

	Framed	Unframed
Shell Tab X	24562	22392
Shell Tab VIII	24554	22384

SHELL TAB X, SHELL TAB VIII

THE RED BIRD

THE BLEW GROSEBEAKE

THE GOLDEN WING'D WOODPECKER

THE AMERICAN PARTRIDGE

THE CHATTERER

THE PARTRIDGE

THE CRESTED JAY

CATESBY BIRD PRINTS

The originals of these individually hand-tinted reproduction prints are based on the work of English naturalist Mark Catesby. Working from his earlier watercolor drawings, Catesby made engravings which were colored by hand, and sold by subscription to a public eager to learn more about America. Catesby traveled extensively in Virginia and the Carolinas between 1712 and 1722, studying and painting a wide variety of flora and fauna.

Framed   18″ × 23″
Unframed   16″ × 21″

	Framed	Unframed
The Red Bird	24927	23234
The Blew Grosebeake	24935	23192
The Golden Wing'd Woodpecker	25106	22962
The American Partridge	24893	23259
The Chatterer	24976	23143
The Partridge	24885	23283
The Crested Jay	25064	23010

ILATHERA DUCK/LITTLE BROWN DUCK

In his travels throughout the colonies, Mark Catesby wrote about his work: "In designing the Plants, I always did them while fresh and just gathered: and the Animals, particularly the Birds, I painted while alive . . . and gave them their gestures peculiar to every kind of Birds, and where it could be admitted, I have adapted the Birds to those Plants on which they fed; or have any relation to."

Framed   22″ × 18″
Unframed   20″ × 16″

	Framed	Unframed
Ilathera Duck	24992	23127
Little Brown Duck	25007	23069

Mark Catesby recorded the wildlife of Williamsburg for his Natural History, *drawing many of the birds and plants that residents and visitors enjoy today.*

ILATHERA DUCK, LITTLE BROWN DUCK

EDWARDS' GOOSE/EDWARDS' DUCK

These "Red-bill's Whistling Duck" and "Canada Goose" prints are reproduced from George Edwards' popular book entitled *A Natural History of Uncommon Birds* published from 1743-1764. 362 hand-colored plates were reproduced from copperplate etchings made by Edwards from his own drawings and offered in as many as four volumes. They feature landscape backgrounds unusual for natural history books of this period.

Framed   12⅜ × 13½"
Unframed 11⅜" × 12½"

	Framed	Unframed
Edwards' Goose	26708	22129
Edwards' Duck	26674	22103

EDWARDS' GOOSE

EDWARDS' DUCK

SWEET WILLIAM

FOUR O'CLOCK IN THE COUNTRY,
FOUR O'CLOCK IN TOWN

SWEET WILLIAM

This print is reproduced from an original hand-colored line engraving by George Townley Stubbs, engraver to His Royal Highness the Prince of Wales. It is based on a painting by Stubbs's father, the famous painter and anatomist of animals. It was published in London on July 30, 1796. Framed 26¾" × 23"   Unframed 24¾" × 21"

Sweet William	Framed 25635	Unframed 22210

NIMROD

FOUR O'CLOCK IN THE COUNTRY/ FOUR O'CLOCK IN TOWN

Satirical prints or cartoons were popular in the eighteenth century. These two etchings by Thomas Rowlandson are rich in detail and offer an amusing commentary on the English countryman's life. They were printed in 1788 and sold to an audience that enjoyed poking fun and pinpointing the foibles of humanity.
Framed 19" × 16"   Unframed 17" × 14"

	Framed	Unframed
Four O'Clock in the Country	25163	22848
Four O'Clock in Town	25148	22855

NIMROD

This political cartoon of George III is reproduced from an eighteenth-century hand-colored etching marked: "Pubd. April ye 20th 1787 by A. Aldbery, Strand London." Colonists collected these provocative and often vulgar satires. A 1766 Williamsburg newspaper advertisement by James McAdam offered a collection of some 200 such prints.
Framed 17" × 14½"   Unframed 15½" × 13"

Nimrod	Framed 26716	Unframed 22061

THE BODLEIAN PLATE

MAP OF VIRGINIA

THE BODLEIAN PLATE

This print is a replica of one taken from an engraved copperplate about 1740. The plate was discovered in the Bodleian Library at Oxford University during the restoration of Williamsburg and provided crucial evidence of the appearance of the city's public buildings in the early eighteenth century.
Framed 19¼″ × 15¾″   Unframed 17¼″ × 13¾″

The Bodleian Plate	Framed 26922	Unframed 22830

MAP OF VIRGINIA

From the mid-sixteenth century onward, maps of Virginia were circulated among Englishmen eager to learn about the New World. Reproduced from an original, this print shows that the boundaries of the Virginia colony changed over time. At one point, it stretched to the Great Lakes and the Mississippi River.
Framed 20″ × 17⅜″
Unframed 18″ × 15⅜″

Map of Virginia	Framed 26955	Unframed 22806

THE FRENCHMAN'S MAP

This print is a replica of a drawing believed to be the work of a French cartographer after the Battle of Yorktown. It shows the city of Williamsburg as it appeared about 1782 and probably served as an aid in billeting the French forces fighting alongside the American Army.
Framed   30″ × 24½″
Unframed 28″ × 22½″

The Frenchman's Map	Framed 26989	Unframed 22780

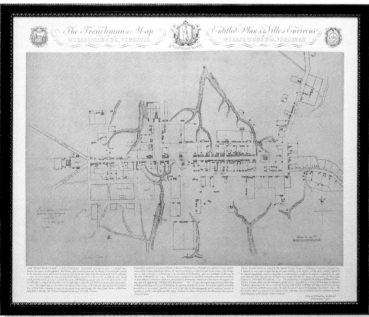

THE FRENCHMAN'S MAP

The Frenchman's Map and the Bodleian Plate were invaluable aids in the restoration of Williamsburg to its eighteenth-century appearance.

Clockwise from top left: THE PRINTING OFFICE, MILLINERY SHOP AND THE GOLDEN BALL SHOP, THE BOOT SHOP AND GREENHOW STORE, STORES ALONG DUKE OF GLOUCESTER STREET

TERRENCE J. COFFMAN PRINTS

These watercolor prints are taken from paintings of buildings along the Duke of Gloucester Street.
Framed   22″ × 18″
Unframed 20″ × 16″

	Framed	Unframed
Printing Office	105866	105874
Millinery and Golden Ball	105882	105890
Stores Along Duke of Gloucester Street	105916	105908
Boot Shop and Greenhow Store	105841	105858

Terrence J. Coffman is the president of the Milwaukee Institute of Art and Design. He has taught watercolor and drawing at the Maryland College of Art and Design and the Smithsonian Institution in Washington, D. C. His work has been featured in numerous one-man shows with exhibits in New York, Baltimore, and Richmond. In recent years, he has specialized in landscapes and historic sites where architecture is a prominent feature.

Joseph Kidd, upholsterer to Lord Botetourt, charged his patron for "brass nailing" the twenty prints in His Lordship's study. Heads of famous philosophers, writers, and artists were considered suitable subjects for gentlemen's studies.

THE SEASONS OF WILLIAMSBURG

Terrence J. Coffman has captured the changing seasons of Williamsburg in a series of limited edition watercolors. 1250 prints of each scene are signed and numbered by the artist. Each features his inventive composition and a sense of visual pleasure.

Framed   26⅞″ × 22″
Unframed   24⅞″ × 20″

	Framed	Unframed
Raleigh Tavern, Spring	27094	22582
Governor's Palace, Spring	26633	22467
Market Square Tavern	27326	24612
Chowning's Tavern, Fall	27151	22541
Governor's Palace, Winter	26617	22483
Wetherburn's Tavern, Winter	27177	22525
King's Arms Tavern, Summer	27128	22566
The Capitol, Spring	27268	22426
Campbell's Tavern	27292	24661

RALEIGH TAVERN, SPRING

GOVERNOR'S PALACE, SPRING

MARKET SQUARE TAVERN

CHOWNING'S TAVERN, FALL

GOVERNOR'S PALACE, WINTER

WETHERBURN'S TAVERN, WINTER

KING'S ARMS TAVERN, SUMMER

THE CAPITOL, SPRING

CAMPBELL'S TAVERN

FOX HUNT: IN FULL CRY

THE CHASE, MAKING A CAST AT A FAULT

WASHINGTON AND LAFAYETTE AT THE BATTLE OF YORKTOWN

EAGLE MILLS, NEW YORK

FOX HUNT: IN FULL CRY

Fox hunting in England dates from at least the fifteenth century and was related to early stag and hare hunting also by hounds. The sport took a more modern form in the nineteenth century, evolving into a national pastime for the upper classes. This print is an interpretation of an oil painting on canvas, circa 1750, by English artist James Seymour. He was well known for his paintings of hunts and racehorses.

THE CHASE

This is one of a set of six interpretive "sporting prints" based on hand-colored line engravings from paintings by James Seymour, engraved by Smith, and printed by Robert Sayer, London, circa 1755.

MAKING A CAST AT A FAULT

The original of this interpretive print is based on a series of hand-colored line engravings by Smith from paintings by James Seymour. The engravings were printed by Robert Sayer in London, England, about 1755.

WASHINGTON AND LAFAYETTE AT THE BATTLE OF YORKTOWN

The Battle of Yorktown was the climax of a brilliantly executed French and American land and sea campaign in the autumn of 1781. It resulted in the surrender of Cornwallis and his army, assuring an American victory in the Revolutionary War. This print is interpreted from an oil painting, probably painted between 1860 and 1880 and attributed to Reuben Law Reed. The original is said to have been based on an account of an eyewitness.

EAGLE MILLS, NEW YORK

Eagle Mills, once known as Millville, is located east of Troy, New York. It was described in 1842 as having 125 residents, 20 houses, a tavern, store, flour mill, sawmill, and carriage manufactory. The original painting of this print was ascribed to Thomas Wilson by earlier owners. A painter by that name lived in Albany and Greenbush between 1847 and 1876 and was described as a "carriage painter" from 1870 to 1876. Some similarity between this painting and the work of Joseph Henry Hidley also has been noted.

THE PEACEABLE KINGDOM OF THE BRANCH

This unusual print is interpreted from an oil painting executed between 1820 and 1830 and attributed to Edward Hicks of Pennsylvania. It takes the figure of a child from a biblical illustration after Richard Westall.

LEEDOM FARM

This print is based on an oil painting by Edward Hicks, then 70 years old, just a few weeks before his death on August 22, 1849. Barely visible on the original is an inscription describing "A May morning view of the Farm and Stock of dl of Newtown Bucks County — Pennsylvania with a representation of Himself. Wife. Father. Mother. Brothers. Sisters and nephew." Leedom inherited the house and other buildings from his parents, Jesse and Mary Twining Leedom, in 1845. Although his parents had died, they were recalled by Hicks in a tribute of love and respect as well as a symbol of continuity.

	Framed	Unframed
Fox Hunt in Full Cry	155267 29¼″ × 23¼″	141226 25¼″ × 19¼″
The Chase	155200 30½″ × 23¼″	141234 27½″ × 20¼″
Making a Cast at a Fault	155259 30½″ × 23¼″	141341 27½″ × 20¼″
Washington and Lafayette at the Battle of Yorktown	27227 27¼″ × 29½″	29710 25¼″ × 28″
Eagle Mills, New York	155275 30½″ × 27¼″	147793 26½″ × 23¼″
The Peaceable Kingdom of the Branch	27573 32½″ × 28½″	33266 26½″ × 22½″
Leedom Farm	162321 34″ × 28″	147801 28″ × 22″

THE PEACEABLE KINGDOM OF THE BRANCH

LEEDOM FARM

Clockwise from top: WHITE BOWL THEOREM, MARY BRADLEY THEOREM/SMALL, BRIGHT FLOWERS THEOREM

THEOREM PRINTS

Theorem painting, or the art of stenciling, flourished in America in the early nineteenth century. Its popularity eventually displaced embroidery to the point where "female academies" instructed fashionable young ladies in using sets of stencils to create paintings on velvet, linen, and paper. Ambitious women kept notebooks and portfolios with their own stencils, design sources, and notes detailing colors and arrangements. Less dedicated women used pre-cut stencils. These prints are taken from early nineteenth-century theorem paintings.

	Framed	Unframed
White Bowl Theorem	172528 9¼″ × 7⅞″	168534 7¼″ × 5⅞″
Mary Bradley Theorem, small	172536 9¼″ × 7⅞″	147868 7¼″ × 5⅞″
Bright Flowers Theorem	172510 9⅜″ × 9⅜″	172569 7⅜″ × 7⅜″
Mary Bradley Theorem, large	155317 24″ × 20″	147850 19½″ × 15½″

MARY BRADLEY THEOREM, LARGE

GIRL IN GARDEN

The original oil on canvas of this print interpretation was painted in America circa 1840. The unknown and untutored artist created a striking painting combining scale and perspective with simplification of form.

	Framed	Unframed
Girl in Garden	133066	116673
	23″ × 32″	17″ × 26″

ROSA HEYWOOD

Rosa Heywood was born in 1834, the only child of Walter and Nancy Foster Heywood of Gardner, Massachusetts. This print is interpreted from an oil painting believed to have been created, circa 1840, possibly in Massachusetts. The unidentified artist employed realistic detail, a variety of textures, rich colors, and a single light source, suggesting some formal training in studio art.

	Framed	Unframed
Rosa Heywood	135582	136077
	23″ × 32″	17″ × 26″

GIRL IN GARDEN, ROSA HEYWOOD

OUTING ON THE HUDSON

The Hudson River offered the dramatic and picturesque natural views popular with nineteenth-century artists. This excursion may have been set in view of the town of Hudson, New York. The original painting, circa 1875, was oil on cardboard. It was found in Woodstock, Ulster County, New York, which accounts for its association with the Hudson River area.

	Framed	Unframed
Outing on the Hudson	155283	147843
	34″ × 28″	28″ × 22″

BABY IN RED CHAIR

This interpretation is based on a painting believed to have been created in Pennsylvania. However, no other works by the unidentified artist have been found to document this.

Baby in Red Chair	Framed	Unframed
Large	26096	32227
	17½″ × 24½″	14½″ × 21½″
Small	119933	80200
	8⅞″ × 11⅛″	5⅞″ × 8⅛″

BABY IN RED CHAIR

OUTING ON THE HUDSON

ORLANDO JONES HOUSE AND GARDEN

ALEXANDER CRAIG GARDEN

BRUTON CHURCH

CAPITOL

GOVERNOR'S PALACE GARDEN

CARTER'S GROVE

GOVERNOR'S PALACE

JOHN BLAIR HERB GARDEN AND KITCHEN

ANNE BELL ROBB'S VIEWS OF WILLIAMSBURG

These simple, charming prints are reminiscent in style of nineteenth-century naive art. Massachusetts artist Anne Bell Robb enjoys traveling and painting historic sites. About Williamsburg, she said that it is "a place set apart in time, preserved . . . where pace is slowed by cobblestone paths and garden fences . . . where past is present."

Framed only 10½″ × 9″

	Framed
Orlando Jones House and Garden	27508
Alexander Craig Garden	27334
Bruton Church	26070
Capitol	27375
Governor's Palace Garden	27425
Carter's Grove	27383
Governor's Palace	27409
John Blair Herb Garden and Kitchen	27441

ORRELL HOUSE AND GOVERNOR'S PALACE POSTERS

These two colorful posters are based on Anne Bell Robb's charming water-color paintings of scenes in Colonial Williamsburg.
Orrell House Poster:
Framed and Unframed 20″ × 24″.
Governor's Palace Poster:
Framed and Unframed 25¾″ × 21″.

	Framed	Unframed
Orrell House Poster	130807	101154
Governor's Palace Poster	177501	171710

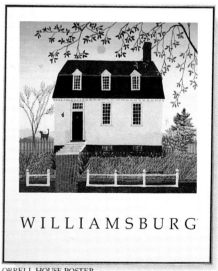

ORRELL HOUSE POSTER

GOVERNOR'S PALACE POSTER

Duke of Gloucester Sampler

This sampler is inspired by the embroidery of schoolgirls in the eighteenth and early nineteenth century. It features an alphabet, numbers, and borders similar to those used to teach young ladies needlework, a skill considered as essential as dancing, drawing, and languages during these times. The scene depicts buildings located along the Duke of Gloucester Street in Colonial Williamsburg. This kit includes pre-printed ivory colored aida cloth, embroidery floss, needle, and instructions. 18″ × 14″. 135350

Farm Sampler

In 1779, Sarah Salter of Marblehead, Massachusetts, completed a handsome sampler using silk thread on tabby-woven linen. This reproduction features a pastoral early summer scene of harmony among the birds and farmyard animals. Sarah's name, age, and birth date have been omitted from the reproduction so that today's needlewoman may embroider her own. This kit includes the sampler stamped on 100% Belgian linen, cotton embroidery floss, needle, and instructions. 16½″ × 16½″. 33993

Chase Sampler

Worked by 11-year-old Mary Starker in 1760, the original of this sampler features a variety of stitches, gay colors, and a forest of flowers and animals. The kit includes the sampler design hand-printed on pure cream-colored linen, cotton embroidery floss, needle, and instructions. 16″ × 24″. 34017

Palace Cross Stitch

The Governor's Palace was the official headquarters and residence of the King of England's deputy in the colony of Virginia. This sampler, inspired by eighteenth- and nineteenth-century samplers in the Colonial Williamsburg collection, combines the image of this historical colonial building with the charm of the sampler form. The kit includes a charted design on beige aida cloth, cotton embroidery floss, needle, and instructions. 12″ × 16″. 183962

Ann Green Sampler

This counted cross stitch sampler is interpreted from an antique dated 1827. The original was stitched by 7-year-old Ann Phillipp Green and features cross stitched embroidery in multi-colored linen thread on handspun and woven linen. The kit includes counted cross stitch fabric, embroidery floss, needle, and instructions. 11″ × 14″. 155341

DUKE OF GLOUCESTER SAMPLER

FARM SAMPLER

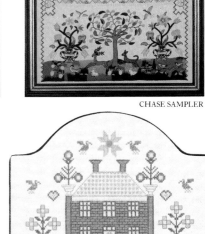

CHASE SAMPLER

PALACE CROSS STITCH

ANN GREEN SAMPLER

The innkeeper's room, Raleigh Tavern.

EIGHTEENTH-CENTURY ARCHITECTURAL
CORNICES
AND CHAIR RAILS

In the eighteenth century moldings served not only decorative purposes in a room but practical ones as well. Cornices defined the transition from wall to ceiling and also covered joints susceptible to cracking. Chair rails protected walls from marks caused by chairs being pushed against them. Moldings also were instrumental in establishing the hierarchy of social spaces. The more elaborate the molding, the more costly it was; consequently, the most embellished room of a building was most important to the owner.

— NICHOLAS A. PAPPAS
Foundation Architect

Shown top to bottom:

NICOLSON HOUSE CORNICE

This Ionic cornice features a handsome modillion block design. It is based on a cornice installed in the mid-eighteenth-century Robert Nicolson House by a later owner. 16340

CARTER'S GROVE™ CHAIR RAIL

Reproduced from the profiles of an original chair rail made about 1751-1753 for the Carter's Grove mansion dining room, this impressive molding features a prominent torus with cymas above and below. 16580

RALEIGH TAVERN CORNICE

Modified from an eighteenth-century design, this molding features a beautifully proportioned dentil course. 16330

ROBERT CARTER HOUSE CHAIR RAIL

The original pre-1746 chair rail on which this design is based features a strongly detailed molding on a beaded rail. 16590

GOVERNOR'S PALACE FRETWORK CORNICE

This interpretation of an eighteenth-century design features a "Wall of Troy" dentil course. 16320

GOVERNOR'S PALACE COVE CORNICE

This design, popular in the late seventeenth and early eighteenth centuries, features an oversize cove molding to extend the height of the cornice. 16310

PEYTON RANDOLPH HOUSE CORNICE

A bed mold, soffit, fascia, and crown mold characterize this cornice, typical of the eighteenth century. 16300

POWELL-HALLAM HOUSE CHAIR RAIL

This reproduction of an original pedestal-cap chair rail found in the Powell-Hallam House features a "Greek-key" design on the fascia. 16160

PEYTON RANDOLPH HOUSE CHAIR RAIL

This classic interpretation of an antique chair rail from the 1715 portion of the Peyton Randolph House features a torus with a cavetto above, and both a cyma and bead below. 16560

WYTHE HOUSE CHAIR RAIL

An asymmetrical group of profiles on a beaded rail characterize this eighteenth-century design. It is an accurate reproduction of the only original portion remaining in the George Wythe House. 16570

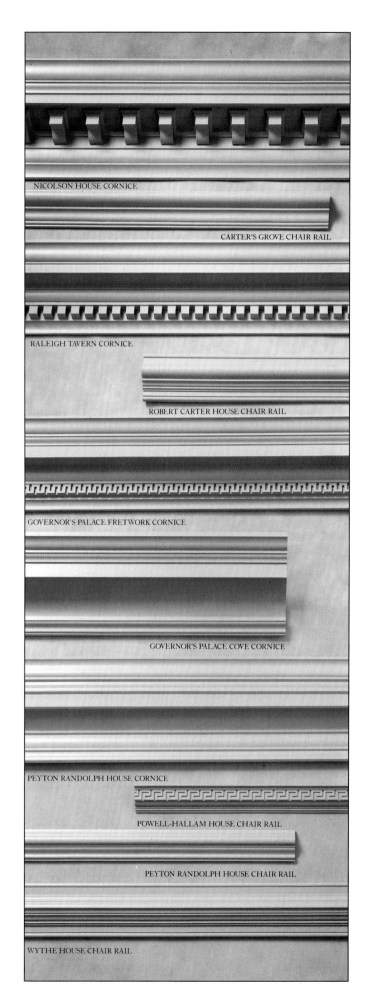

NICOLSON HOUSE CORNICE

CARTER'S GROVE CHAIR RAIL

RALEIGH TAVERN CORNICE

ROBERT CARTER HOUSE CHAIR RAIL

GOVERNOR'S PALACE FRETWORK CORNICE

GOVERNOR'S PALACE COVE CORNICE

PEYTON RANDOLPH HOUSE CORNICE

POWELL-HALLAM HOUSE CHAIR RAIL

PEYTON RANDOLPH HOUSE CHAIR RAIL

WYTHE HOUSE CHAIR RAIL

EIGHTEENTH-CENTURY
FIREPLACE ACCESSORIES

The vast forests of eighteenth-century America provided fuel for colonial hearths long after Englishmen had replaced andirons with grates for heating and cooking. Colonial blacksmiths and brass founders continued to make andirons, which represent some of the most significant products, both technically and aesthetically, of their trades. Well-appointed fireplaces in affluent households were usually equipped with a pair of andirons, a set of fire tools held by jamb hooks, a pierced fender to protect floors from fire, and a cast-iron fireback to protect masonry from the heat.

— JOHN D. DAVIS
Senior Curator
Curator of Metalwork

CW1605R

JAMB HOOKS

Chimney hooks were used during the eighteenth century to hold fire tools and usually were located on each side of the fireplace. Although they were used rarely in England, they were made there in large quantities for export to America. These brass reproduction jamb hooks are based on antiques found in the Brush-Everard House in Williamsburg. CW1605L CW1605R

Shown clockwise: BALL FIRE TOOLS, CHARLES REX FIREBACK, CLAW AND BALL ANDIRON, and SERPENTINE FENDER

SERPENTINE FENDER

"Fend-irons" were used to hold back burning embers during the eighteenth century. They originated in Europe and their development paralleled that of the fire grate. Early examples were made of iron. The antique of this reproduction was made in England about 1780. It features intricately pierced brass, a scalloped edge, and a graceful shape. Height 6¾"; Length 49¼". CW102-1

PANEL FIREBACK

Shown left to right: DAVIS, CLAW AND BALL, BALL, and RALEIGH TAVERN FINIALS

VIRGINIA FIREBACK, DAVIS ANDIRONS

Shown left to right: RALEIGH TAVERN ANDIRONS, CHARLES REX FIREBACK, RALEIGH TAVERN FIRE TOOLS

FIRE TOOLS

High-style brass and polished steel "fire-irons" were made in sets with each implement having matching ornamentation. These reproductions are slightly larger than tools of modern design. Three of the brass finial designs have matching andirons. Average height 29".

CW 103-1A Davis fire tools
CW 103-1B Claw and ball fire tools
CW 103-1 Ball fire tools
CW 103-1C Raleigh Tavern fire tools

ANDIRONS

Elaborately decorated andirons usually were used in the parlor. The claw and ball design is reproduced from late eighteenth-century brass originals made in Pennsylvania. The Davis andirons are reproduced in sand-cast brass from antiques, circa 1803-1823, marked "J. Davis, Boston." The Raleigh Tavern andirons are reproduced in brass from early nineteenth-century originals made by John Bailey of New York City.

CW 100-1 Claw-and-ball andirons — Height 24"; Depth 22½"
CW 100-4 Davis andirons — Height 17"; Depth 15½"
CW 100-2 Raleigh Tavern andirons — Height 23½"; Depth 22"

FIREBACKS

Firebacks were developed in fifteenth-century Europe to help radiate heat from the hearth. The Charles Rex fireback is reproduced from an antique made in the second quarter of the seventeenth century and bears the royal arms of King Charles I of England. The Panel fireback is reproduced from an original cast made at the Chiswell Furnace in Hanover County, Virginia, about 1740. The Virginia fireback is a cast-iron reproduction taken from eighteenth-century fragments excavated in Williamsburg.

CW 101-1 Charles Rex fireback — Height 23"; Width 21"
CW 101-3 Panel fireback — Height 24"; Width 18½"
CW 101-2 Virginia fireback — Height 24"; Width 20¾"

JAMES GEDDY HOUSE MANTEL

Mrs. James Geddy and her mother-in-law could enjoy a cup of tea in the parlor of their house on the Duke of Gloucester Street.

JAMES GEDDY HOUSE MANTEL

The Geddy House, which dates from the 1760s, was both the home and shop of a successful family of craftsmen whose trades included those of gunsmith, silversmith, founder, cutler, blacksmith, jeweler, and engraver. This solid wood mantel is reproduced from the original in the house. Its detailing is similar to some eighteenth-century marble mantels. CW1475

WILLIAM BYRD III MANTEL

William Byrd III, son of the illustrious builder of the magnificent James River plantation Westover, purchased his Williamsburg house from William Allen in 1772. The original of this reproduction mantel dates from about 1770. The hand-carved woven detail under the mantel shelf probably was copied from eighteenth-century architectural pattern books. It features a fluted columnar pilaster as well as concave, convex, and flat surfaces characteristic of the period. CW1476

WILLIAM BYRD III MANTEL

BRASS RIM LOCKS

Rim locks received their name because their design exposes the entire lock. Reproduced from hardware excavated at the Governor's Palace site and found on other structures in Williamsburg, all of these rim locks are cast in heavy brass and are hand-polished to add classic eighteenth-century beauty to a paneled door. The steel mechanism is hand-fitted by expert craftsmen. The locks are available in three sizes to fit the scale of a wide range of doors.

Lock 1 — Height 5¾"; Width 10"; Depth 1⅜"

Lock 2 — Height 4½"; Width 8"; Depth 1"

Lock 3 (interior door only) — Height 4"; Width 6¼"; Depth ⅞"

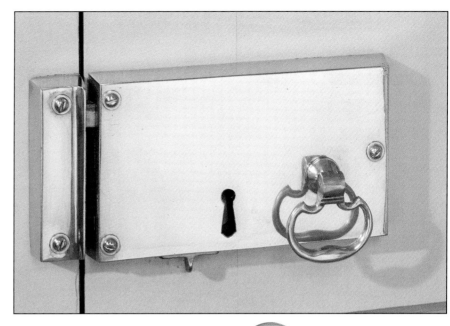

KEYS, KNOBS/HANDLES, AND CYLINDERS

A brass or stainless steel key comes with each lock. One or two knobs and/or drop handles can be used on the inside or outside of any size lock. The no. 1 and no. 2 locks are available with a modern key cylinder. The modern cylinder, shown at the far right, offers the advantage of the use of a standard key.

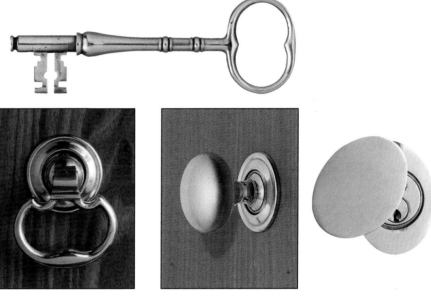

BRASS HINGES

These sandcast solid brass hinges are based on early eighteenth-century hardware found on houses in Williamsburg. Each hinge is filed and polished by hand and finished with special tarnish-resistant lacquer. The H hinge is an adaptation of the HL antique. Both are available in the original 11¾" size or adapted in an 8¾" size for many modern doors. The mortise hinge is adapted from one found on the Peyton Randolph House.

HL1 – Height 11¾"; Width 14⅞'
HL2 – Height 8¼"; Width 11¼"
H1 – Height 11¾"; Width 4½"
H2 – Height 8¾"; Width 3¼"
BF1 Mortise hinge – Height 4¼"

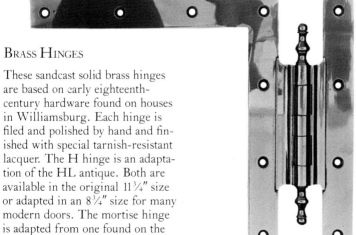
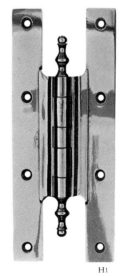
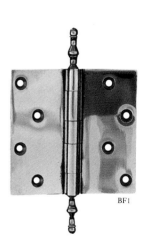

HL1   H1

BF1

"S" Door Knocker

This graceful design is reproduced from an original discovered on an eighteenth-century house on Duke of Gloucester Street. Its distinctive shape is duplicated by using the same process as was employed to make the original. Molten metal is cast into a sand mold made from the antique. Since the original is slightly off-center, so is the reproduction. Height 7¾"; Width 2¼"; Projection 2¾". CW 17-68

CW 17-68

Urn Door Knocker

Although much ornamental brass was imported by Williamsburg merchants, some was made in local foundries such as that operated around 1751 by David and William Geddy. Even the most familiar objects reflected the eighteenth-century taste for symmetry and proportion, as exemplified by the classic urn shape of this brass door knocker. Its design is derived from a late eighteenth-century antique. Height 7¾"; Width 4¼". CW 17-67

CW 17-67

Doors

Doors such as this are adapted with molding profiles and panel configurations typical of eighteenth-century construction. Interior doors feature raised decorative panels on the front and flat practical panels on the back. Single panel doors are available in standard widths measuring one to two feet. Double panel doors in standard widths measure two to three feet. Exterior doors are manufactured in three different panel designs and offered with or without an eighteenth-century style transom. Tenon and peg construction, typical of the period, is used for all doors. Each design is adapted in size and thickness for modern use.

EIGHTEENTH-CENTURY
EXTERIOR PAINTS

These exterior paints represent visual matching of colors found in Williamsburg and the tidewater area of Virginia during the early years of the Restoration.

— NICHOLAS A. PAPPAS
Foundation Architect

Elizabeth Carlos House,
Williamsburg, Virginia

Market Square Tavern Shell
W81-0330

Market Square Tavern Gray
W82-0270

Bracken Tenement Biscuit
W81-1064

Grissell Hay Lodging House Green
W81-1061

Bracken Tenement Blue Slate
W83-1065

William Byrd III House Ivory
W81-1073

Ludwell Tenement Sage
W82-1079

Robert Carter Tobacco
W84-0230

James Moir Shop Fawn
W82-1080

Barraud House Green
W83-1062

Palace Arms Red
W1083 (Package Color)

Brush-Everard Gold
W82-1067

Governor's Palace Tan
W82-1072

Nicolson Store Red
W86-1081

Grissell Hay Lodging House Gold
W83-1060

George Pitt House Green
W84-1088

Levingston Kitchen Green
W84-1077

Holt's Storehouse Gray
W82-1074

William Finnie House Brown
W85-0225

Ludwell Tenement Gold
W83-1078

Benjamin Powell House Green
W85-1089

George Davenport House Green
W85-1071

Peyton Randolph Gray
W82-1086

Palmer House Kitchen Brown
W85-1085

George Pitt House Caramel
W84-1087

Palmer House Green
W84-1084

Market Square Tavern Dark Green
W85-0620

King's Arms Tavern Gray
W83-1076

Bryan House Chocolate
W85-1068

Nicolson Store Taupe
W83-1082

James Geddy Green
W84-1075

Burdett's Ordinary Black Green
W85-0625

Purdie House Gray Slate
W83-1090

Chowning's Tavern Brown
W85-1070

Raleigh Tavern Sorrel
W83-1091

Colors shown above are available in Satin Gloss Latex House Paint.

The inventory of the possessions of Lord Botetourt, Virginia's penultimate royal governor, richly details the furnishings of the Palace in 1770. Numerous items were intended for tea drinking, including a large silver tea board or tray, silver sugar tongs and teaspoons, a silver-plated tea kitchen or urn, an Oriental blue-and-white porcelain tea service (among others), japanned tea chests, iron sugar hatchets, and large canisters for tea. Records indicate that hyson tea was the governor's preference.

Accessories above shown this section.

ACCESSORIZING
IN THE TWENTIETH CENTURY

*W*illiamsburg Reproductions cover the table with an array of dining and entertaining styles. Those whose tastes lean toward the formal can choose from elegant china and sterling patterns, handsome drinking goblets, and exquisite linens, with silver, brass, and porcelain decorative accents for the table's center. More casual lifestyles may prefer the selections of tavern dinnerware and pewter that move so easily from kitchen to dining room to bar.

Both brides and experienced hostesses can rest assured that these timeless designs will never become outmoded, nor will their classic styling tire the eye in years to come. After a lifetime of service, *Williamsburg* Reproductions will be ready to pass along to the twenty-first century, when future generations can cherish them again.

Virtually all accoutrements necessary for a proper tea were imported to the colonies from England. Here a table in the Everards' parlor is set with "tortoiseshell ware" from the Staffordshire potteries, silver sugar tongs from a London factory, and a japanned hot water kettle from Pontypool in Wales. Growing English industries were making such wares available to a wide consumer market by the second half of the eighteenth century.

DINING
IN THE EIGHTEENTH CENTURY

A beautiful display on the dining table when guests and family entered the room was a requirement in the eighteenth century, as it is today, for the beginning of a successful party. When one entered the dining room a great and glorious array of food — fast getting cold — had already been placed on the table. Soup was served from tureens resting at one or both ends of the table, depending on the size of the dinner party, while between there was a display of red and white meats, fish, breads, sauces, vegetables according to the season, and condiments of all kinds. Symmetry was required — a leg of lamb might balance a haunch of venison and a turkey balance a ham. At the corners in sets of four might be meat pies and pickled or fresh vegetables.

The dinnerware could be the most elegant silver or silver gilt, fine porcelain from the Orient or England, cream-ware, called "Queens China" in Williamsburg, or even cruder delftware. Whatever the material, eighteenth-century services contained many of the forms found today. Although the plates, dishes, and platters of the eighteenth-century dinner service varied only slightly from ours today, the numbers in a service would not be the same. A service might have had one dish of the largest size, two dishes each of the next sizes down, and four each of the smaller sizes. There would be sauceboats, salts, and tureens. Usually there were twice as many dinner plates as soup plates, probably due to the English custom (sometimes practiced in the American colonies) of having a sec-

ond course before the dessert, which consisted of lighter meats along with jellies and puddings.

Tea and coffee were served in another room after dinner so the tea and coffee wares could be an entirely different pattern from the dinner service. Since everything was removed from the table after the main course was completed, it was not necessary for the dessert dishes to be the same or a complementary pattern.

The dessert, the last and most showy course, was set much like the main course, that is, the sizes and shapes of the dishes had to balance. The dessert service could be the most exotic, the plates very colorful and the dishes of unusual shapes, often oval or square or formed like various kinds of vegetation such as cabbage or fig leaves. The length of the table held fruits (fresh, candied, or dried), tarts, cakes, puddings, trifle, nuts, and jellies and syllabubs in specially formed glasses. Candies such as marzipan were displayed in small dishes carefully placed to enhance the design of the table. A silver epergne filled with fruit and sweetmeats — or a pyramid of glass stands stacked with things both to eat and for show — provided the focal point in the center of the table.

Hannah Glasse, an English cookbook author, described a pyramid in *The Compleat Confectioner:* "Two salvers one above another, whip'd syllabubs and jellies intermix'd with crisp'd almonds, and little ratafia cakes, one little one above all, with preserved orange or pine apples, little bottles with flowers to

adorn'd it, and knicknacks strew'd about the salver." Porcelain figures were sometimes used in and around the centerpiece. Sometimes a centerboard — with mirrors imitating ponds, mica and other small stones representing paths on which figures walked, and clumps of moss appearing as small hillocks on which porcelain animals grazed — was used. Such elaborate setups would have remained on the table through the entire meal.

Dinner, served in the early afternoon, would not require the use of candlesticks. A supper served about eight p.m. was normally a much lesser meal, both in show and in food served, the fare often being leftovers from the earlier dinner. A supper during a party or ball, on the other hand, could be as showy as a dinner. It would be one course, incorporating the sweets and jellies of the dessert with some light meats. The fanciest china and silver would be used incorporating many pieces from the dessert service.

As today, the table china fit the personality of the family and the fashion with the more massive delft of the earlier baroque period, the elaborate English porcelain in the rococo, and the more austere, perhaps undecorated, creamware or "Queen's China" in the neo-classical period at the end of the eighteenth century.

— JOHN C. AUSTIN

John C. Austin, *senior curator and curator of ceramics and glass, is the author of* Chelsea Porcelain at Williamsburg. *He is preparing a catalog of the delft-ware in the collection.*

Right: jelly glasses on a dessert pyramid at the Palace; middle: a seated ball supper at the Palace; bottom: a collation served as refreshment during a ball at the Peyton Randolph house.

EIGHTEENTH-CENTURY
CHINA

Starting in the middle of the eighteenth century, fine porcelain of several varieties was produced in England to compete with that imported from China and to grace the tables of merchants, gentry, and the nobility. By the beginning of the next century, a very fine variety, called bone china, evolved and became the premier porcelain of England as it is still today.

—JOHN C. AUSTIN
Senior Curator
Curator of Ceramics and Glass

CHINESE FLOWERS

CHINESE TIGER

CUCKOO

"CHINESE FLOWERS" BONE CHINA DINNERWARE

Developed at the end of the eighteenth century in England, bone china soon became immensely popular. Among the nineteenth-century manufacturers was Josiah Wedgwood II, son of the man who founded the famous Wedgwood factory in Burslem in 1759. This handsome design is adapted from an eighteenth-century pattern.

"CHINESE TIGER" BONE CHINA DINNERWARE

Made of clay and feldspathic rock with about 50 percent calcinated cattle bones, bone china became the standard ware of fine English porcelain factories in the 1800s because of its delicate translucence. This "dogs-of-fo" Chinese decoration was called Chinese Tiger in the early nineteenth century and was produced in green, red, blue, and black patterns by the Wedgwood factory about 1815.

Plate — dinner, salad/dessert, bread and butter   Rim soup   Cream soup cup and saucer   Platter — 14" or 12"

BIANCA

"CUCKOO" BONE CHINA DINNERWARE

Heavily influenced by oriental motifs, the chinoiserie decoration on this dinnerware is based on a Wedgwood bone china cup and saucer now in the Colonial Williamsburg Collection. This dinnerware may have appeared on tables in moderately affluent homes in the early nineteenth century.

"BIANCA" BONE CHINA DINNERWARE

Potteries were scattered throughout England by the beginning of the nineteenth century. One of them, New Hall, was a Staffordshire neighbor of Wedgwood and produced the central motif of this pattern in several versions. Here it has been combined with two others of the period to create the delicate Bianca pattern.

Covered
vegetable dish

Open
vegetable dish

Sauceboat
and stand

Bowl — 10″ or 8″

Coffeepot

Sugar box

Creamer

After-dinner
cup and saucer

Teacup
and saucer

Teapot

259

"POTPOURRI" DINNERWARE

Queen's Ware, Josiah Wedgwood's famous cream colored earthenware, achieved instant popularity. It was named in honor of Queen Charlotte, wife of George III, who fancied this thin yet durable new ceramic. Plates and flat dishes in the Queen's Shape have been manufactured continuously at the Wedgwood factory since 1765. The other forms were invented in the early twentieth century. Shards found at archaeological excavations in Williamsburg were usually plain. Potpourri's rich pattern is interpreted from an eighteenth-century textile and is transfer-printed onto the creamware.

Plate — dinner, salad/dessert, bread and butter

Soup plate

Soup cup and saucer

Fruit saucer

Oatmeal saucer

Teacup and saucer

Coffee cup and saucer

Square cake plate

Cream

Josiah Wedgwood's cream-colored earthenware, called "Queen's china" after Queen Charlotte granted him her patronage, was the most popular ceramic ware of the 1770s. Fragments of it have been excavated from many sites in Williamsburg. Here a service decorated with transfer prints of exotic birds makes a festive Christmas table at the George Wythe House.

Sugar box   Teapot   Coffeepot   Fruit/Salad bowl   Open vegetable dish, oval   Covered vegetable dish   Sauceboat and stand   Platter — 14" or 12" (Round platter also available 12") see pg. 258

CHRISTIANA CAMPBELL'S TAVERN WITH CHECKED LINENS SHOWN ON PAGE 265.

TAVERNWARE

Tavernware is based on period delft designs that have been interpreted for modern dinnerware. Plates take the form and shape of delft plates of the period while hollowwares, such as teacups and teapots, have been adapted for more modern requirements. Tavernware is decorated with elements from eighteenth-century patterns and is used in the taverns operating today in the Historic Area of Williamsburg.

Particular curatorial care went into the selection of accurate furnishings of Colonial Williamsburg's newest restaurant, Shields Tavern. The dinnerware is based on shards of fish-decorated delft found on the site.

SHIELDS TAVERN

CHRISTIANA CAMPBELL'S TAVERN™ DINNERWARE

This charming blue and white pattern, incorporating a squirrel with grapevine, is based on fragments of a delft plate discovered in Williamsburg. It is a variation of a familiar Chinese pattern, indicating the fascination with Oriental motifs in England and the colonies during the eighteenth century. This dinnerware is available in two plate sizes, as well as a platter, bowl, bouillon cup, teacup, saucer, teapot, and cream jug.

SHIELDS TAVERN™ DINNERWARE

Based on a delft plate probably made in London during the 1740s, the design of this dinnerware service is interpreted from a plate in the Colonial Williamsburg collection which relates to fragments found on the actual site of Shields Tavern in Williamsburg. This interpretation incorporates unusual design elements such as the manganese purple ground and the blue fish. It is available in two plate sizes, as well as a platter, bowl, bouillon cup, teacup, saucer, teapot, and cream jug.

CHOWNING'S TAVERN™ DINNERWARE

This colorful dinnerware pattern is an interpretation of an English delft plate made in Bristol, England, circa 1730. The peacock is copied from a multicolored fragment unearthed in Williamsburg during archaeological excavations. Peacock plates in the Colonial Williamsburg collection provided the added documentation needed to copy the complete design accurately. This tavernware is available in two plate sizes, as well as a platter, bowl, bouillon cup, saucer, teacup, teapot, and cream jug.

CHOWNING'S TAVERN

GOVERNOR'S PALACE

*Lord Botetourt's extensive collection of silver at the
Governor's Palace contained a silver writing stand with
a bell for summoning servants and two casters.*

CW24-76

"GOVERNOR'S PALACE" TABLE LINENS

This intricately woven design is reproduced from a white linen damask tablecloth in the Colonial Williamsburg collection. The original was made in the British Islands or the Low Countries, circa 1780-1800.

Placemat	15″ × 20″	74487
Napkin	24″ × 24″	73396
Tablecloth	72″ × 72″	73397
	with 4 napkins	80543
Tablecloth	72″ × 98″	73398
	with 6 napkins	80544
Tablecloth	72″ × 110″	73399
	with 8 napkins	80545
Tablecloth	72″ × 128″	73400
	with 10 napkins	80546
Tablecloth	72″ × 146″	73401
	with 12 napkins	80547

BRASS BELL

Reproduced from an English "hand bell" circa 1770, a bell such as this was useful for many household activities involving both staff and family. Small hand bells were often a part of desk and writing equipment. CW24-76

CHECKED LINENS

A linen cushion cover in the Colonial Williamsburg collection was the inspiration for these linens. In the eighteenth century, checked textiles often were used for slipcovers and bed curtains, while tablecloths usually were made of white linen.

	Blue	Red
Tablecloth	23902	23901
Placemat	15902	15901
Napkin	21902	21901

"CORNFLOWERS" TABLE LINENS

These linens are interpreted from a blue and white damask tablecloth made in Germany in 1775. Most expensive damask tablecloths were part of a set woven on complex draw-looms, then imported to the colonies from England or the Low Countries. Napkin and placemat available in rose or blue.

CHECKED

"CORNFLOWERS"

EIGHTEENTH-CENTURY
SILVER FLATWARE

Matched sets of elegant sterling flatware came into general use in the early eighteenth century. They have been important ever since as expressions of taste and gentility.

— JOHN D. DAVIS
Senior Curator
Curator of Metalwork

"SHELL" STERLING SILVER FLATWARE

This lovely silver pattern is based on a set of antique flatware made in England about 1760. The raised shell is a common eighteenth-century motif. During the middle of the century, it was used on English-made goods of every description, especially silver. Original pieces used for reproduction include knives and various sizes of spoons and forks. Other forms, such as the iced tea spoon, were unknown in the eighteenth century and have been adapted to complete the set.

GS-69	Baby Fork
GS-11	Cocktail/Oyster Fork
GS-10	Salad/Dessert Fork
GS-9	Dinner Fork
GS-7	Butter Spreader
GS-61	Steak Knife
GS-1	Dinner Knife
GS-5	Tablespoon
GS-13	Iced Tea Spoon
GS-4	Service Spoon
GS-12	Teaspoon
GS-68	Baby Spoon
GS-8	Coffee Spoon
GS-54	Salt Spoon

Shown left to right:

GS-64	Butter Server or Fish Knife
GS-60	Cold Meat Fork
GS-63	Gravy Ladle
GS-70	Sugar Shell

RT-68, RT-69

"Queen Anne" Sterling Silver Flatware

Introduced over fifty years ago, this classic flatware design was one of the first reproductions of eighteenth-century items commissioned by Colonial Williamsburg. Among the original prototypes is a coffee spoon found during archaeological excavations of the Raleigh Tavern in 1930. The rat-tailed spoons, three-tined forks, pistol-handled knives, and serving pieces are reproductions of antiques from 1720-1770 and have been recognized for the excellence of their execution. Each piece is reproduced to the precise weight distribution tolerances achieved by eighteenth-century silversmiths for balance and comfort in the hand.

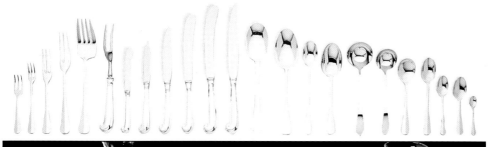

RT-69	Baby Fork
RT-11	Cocktail/Oyster Fork
RT-10	Salad/Dessert Fork
RT-9	Dinner Fork
RT-60	Cold Meat Fork
RT-14	Roast Carving Fork — 2 pc. set
RT-7	Butter Spreader
RT-64	Fish Knife/Butter Server
RT-61	Steak Knife
RT-3	Dinner Knife — small
RT-1	Dinner Knife — large
RT-62	Steak Carving Knife — 2 pc. set
RT-6	Notched Tablespoon
RT-5	Tablespoon
RT-13	Iced Tea Spoon
RT-4	Service Spoon
RT-63	Ladle — large
RT-51	Ladle — small
RT-70	Sugar Shell
RT-12	Teaspoon
RT-8	Coffee Spoon
RT-68	Baby Spoon
RT-54	Salt Spoon

EIGHTEENTH-CENTURY
CRYSTAL

Crystal, a natural transparent stone that was formed into vessels and cut to become chandelier prisms, has in modern times given its name to the fine lead glass produced in England since the end of the seventeenth century. During the eighteenth century while the English were producing this highly reflective ware, the glass factories in Europe were producing a less brilliant soda glass. Period documents and colonial archaeological finds tell us that this seemingly fragile ware was shipped to the colonies for tables in taverns, houses, and the royal governor's residence.

—JOHN C. AUSTIN
Senior Curator
Curator of Ceramics and Glass

Left to right: CW3W, CW3G, CW3S

AIR-TWIST STEMWARE

These hand-made lead crystal goblets and sherbets are reproduced from eighteenth-century antiques as well as fragments found during archaeological excavations at Williamsburg. The wine glass is an adaptation. The distinctive "worm'd" decoration in the stem was made by inserting a wire into molten glass to form an air bubble or fistula, then twisting it into a spiral shape with wooden paddles and other special tools. This design came into fashion around 1740.

CW3W   Air-Twist Wine
CW3G   Air-Twist Goblet
CW3S   Air-Twist Sherbet
CW47   Air-Twist Bell-shaped
            Wine/Goblet

CW47

LEAD CRYSTAL PITCHER

Three attempts to establish a glass-blowing industry in Virginia during the seventeenth century proved less than successful. As a result, most crystal was imported from England. This 32 percent lead crystal pitcher was reproduced from an English original circa 1750. It is made using the same basic tools and techniques as the original. 7⅞" tall; 1½ qts. CW38P

CW38P

Left to right: CW1S, CW1G, CW1W   Left to right: CW2W, CW2G, CW2S

BALUSTER STEMWARE

The classic ornamental shape of the wine glass was reproduced from an English design from the first half of the eighteenth century. It features a sloping dome foot and inverted baluster, with the knop at the top of the stem. Goblet and sherbet forms have been adapted from this shape.

CW1W   Baluster Wine
CW1G   Baluster Goblet
CW1S   Baluster Sherbet

TEARDROP STEMWARE

The wine glass and goblet are reproduced from an eighteenth-century shape known as a sweet-meat glass, now termed a champagne glass. The modern sherbet form is an adaptation. Each piece is individually mouth-blown and hand-formed. A wire is inserted into the molten stem to form a hollow channel. Application of a wet stick creates steam, forming the tear.

CW2W   Teardrop Wine
CW2G   Teardrop Goblet
CW2S   Teardrop Sherbet
CW2P   Teardrop Pilsner

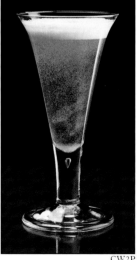

CW2P

Wines and spirits from Lord Botetourt's well-stocked cellars were drunk in style at the Governor's Palace. His Lordship's pantry shelves held several dozen decanters and over a hundred wine glasses, some described as "flowered," meaning engraved.

Left to right: CW6, CW13, CW42S, CW122, CW5S

DECANTERS

Virginians in the eighteenth century enjoyed both locally made and imported wines. Since sediment was often found in the original bottles, wine was decanted. Decanters also held wine drawn from large casks or barrels. These three decanter designs are reproduced from English originals made at the end of the eighteenth century or the beginning of the nineteenth century. CW6 Square Decanter 1½ qts.   CW42S Decanter 1¼ qts. CW13 Tall Crystal Decanter 1⅓ qts.

STERLING SILVER DECANTER LABELS

The design and lettering style of these silver decanter labels are reproduced from originals such as those "18 Silver bottle Labells" kept with the "Plate, in the Pantry" at the Governor's Palace in 1770. There are labels for more modern spirits as well as eighteenth-century favorites such as port, sherry, and brandy.

RT37	Rye Label	RT42	Brandy Label
RT38	Scotch Label	RT43	Gin Label
RT39	Bourbon Label	RT44	Rum Label
RT40	Port Label	RT45	Vodka Label
RT41	Sherry Label	RT46	Plain Label

Top J21, Bottom RT39

BOTTLE TICKETS

These silverplate decanter labels are adapted from a silver wine label or "bottle ticket" made in England about 1740. Popularity of this item paralleled the increased interest in a variety of wines and development of the glass decanter.

J19	Bourbon Bottle Ticket	J22	Vodka Bottle Ticket
J20	Gin Bottle Ticket	J23	Set of Four Bottle Tickets
J21	Scotch Bottle Ticket		

CW5S

GALLERY TRAY

This tray is reproduced from an eighteenth-century tea board and was used primarily for serving tea. It is cut from solid mahogany and has a handsomely pierced rim with convenient hand-carved hand holes. Only the modern heat- and alcohol-resistant finish differentiates this tray from the original. CW120

BOTTLE STAND

Bottle stands protected the tabletop while facilitating movement of decanters among guests. This adaptation is based on an English wine coaster made in the late eighteenth century. The antique is made using a molded base with two strips of mahogany glued together and applied as a rim. The adaptation is shaped from a single piece of wood. CW122

CRYSTAL CORDIALS

Eighteenth-century tavern keepers in Virginia had a wide selection of glass, pewter, and delft drinking wares on hand to accommodate their patrons. Among them may have been lead crystal tumblers such as these, based on fragments uncovered during archaeological excavations in Williamsburg. Height 2⅞". CW5S

CW120

CW24-80, CW126

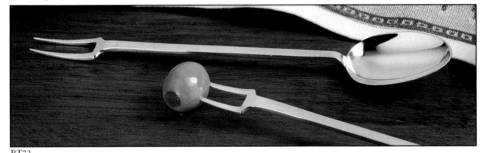

RT72

WINE SERVER

An interest in wines led to the creation of a host of service and storage accessories. A wine cradle such as this, with built-in drip-tray, showed the bottle to advantage. Reproduced from an eighteenth-century original, this handsome wine server is cut from select mahogany, assembled in the manner of the antique, and hand-rubbed to enhance the grain of the wood. CW126

CORKSCREW

This brass and steel corkscrew is reproduced from an eighteenth-century English antique. The original probably received much use considering the fondness of the English and their colonial counterparts for wine and other spirits. CW24-80

SUCKET FORK

"Suckets" were popular sweet-meats made of fruit preserved in sugar and sometimes flavored with spirits. This sterling silver reproduction is based on a rare antique made in London in 1674 or 1675. The fork was used to spear the fruit while the spoon end was used to eat the syrup. RT72

William Marshman, Lord Bote-tourt's steward, oversaw house-hold operations at the Palace and secured the silver and glassware in his pantry domain.

PEWTER CUPS

Reproduced from an early eighteenth-century pewter beaker, this pewter cup was an ideal vessel for holding possets, punches, caudles, juleps and other drinks made of wine and spirits that were popular in colonial Virginia.
CW49 Pewter Cup – 8 oz.
CW49M Small Pewter Cup – 2 oz.

CW49

CW49M

DELFT MUGS

Adapted from an eighteenth-century English mug, these vessels are ideal for serving cold refreshments. The original is a larger, quart-size mug bearing the word "Porter," a thick malt beverage popular with laborers in the 1700s.

C90A Delft Mug – Ale
C90B Delft Mug – Beer
C90C Delft Mug – Cyder

PEWTER CORDIAL CUP

This cup was adapted from an antique beaker made in Holland. Such beakers were used for both domestic and ecclesiastical purposes during the eighteenth century. This version makes an excellent cordial.

CW88M Cordial cup – 2¼″ high; 1 oz.

Left to right: C90B, C90A, C90C

CW88M

PEWTER TANKARD AND QUART PITCHER

Jefferson, Washington, and Madison may well have enjoyed their full-bodied porters, beers, and ales in eighteenth-century bellied mugs such as this. The ale jug, from the early nineteenth century, features a straight neck and high shoulders.

CW55 Pewter Tankard – 5″ high; 16 oz.
CW100 Pewter Quart Pitcher – 5½″ high; 36 oz.

Left to right: CW55, CW100

273

Clockwise from left: CW38, CW57, CW95, CW1S, C44

Arrack punch was the house specialty at Henry Wetherburn's tavern. His estate inventory listed seven china bowls, which were probably for punch.

DELFT PUNCH BOWL

The original of this reproduction was used to hold punch, a beverage concocted from distilled liquor, citrus juice, spices, sugar, and water. Archaeologists unearthed the original bowl fragment, now restored, during excavations at the site of John Coke's tavern near the Capitol. Diameter: 10½″. C44

PEWTER PITCHER

Large baluster jugs such as this were generally used to serve beer, a favorite of American colonists in the eighteenth century. Many hard-working Virginians brewed their own short-lived small or middling beer. Stronger Welsh ale as well as London and Bristol beer were imported by the barrel. The silver original of this pewter adaptation is attributed to London silversmith Samuel Hitchcock and was made in 1728-1729. Height 9½″; 90 oz. CW95

DELFT MUGS

Most eighteenth-century mugs were designed to hold brown porter, a thick malt beverage invented near London about 1720 by brewer Ralph Harwood. The name, short for porter's ale or beer, is derived from its popularity with laborers and other hard-working people. An inventory of the Raleigh Tavern in 1771 noted 23 dozen bottles of porter in the cellar.
C54   Delft Mug – 12 oz.
C58   Delft Mug – 12 oz.
C59   Delft Porter Mug – quart

DELFT PUNCH BOWL

Proposing toasts was a popular custom when Virginians gathered in taverns for an evening of good-fellowship. Punch, a popular eighteenth-century drink made of distilled spirits such as arrack, brandy, or rum mixed with citrus juice, sugar, and water, may well have been mixed in a bowl such as this. It holds a full quart and is reproduced from a mid-eighteenth-century Bristol delft bowl. No doubt many arrangements and special arrangements were celebrated over "one bowl more . . . ." C79

Left to right: C54, C59, C58

C79

Clockwise from left: CW2441, CW2447, CW2443, CW2446, CW2445

CW2440

"CHELSEA BIRD" PORCELAIN PLATES

These lovely plates are reproduced from antiques made between 1758 and 1769 by the Chelsea Porcelain Manufactory near London. This factory produced some of England's finest porcelain, using a warm colored paste, gifted modelers, and decorators sensitive to the scale and qualities of the medium. The birds may have been painted in the London workshop of gifted ceramics decorator James Giles. CW2440 set of four

"EXOTIC BIRDS" PORCELAIN ACCESSORIES

The fabulous bird in these accessories is interpreted from a set of porcelain plates made by the Chelsea Porcelain Manufactory near London between 1758 and 1769. James Giles, an independent ceramics decorator, may have added the bright enamel colors to the originals in his London workshop. Each of these interpretive accessories replicates a traditional shape of eighteenth-century serving pieces.

CW2441 Shell dish – white tail feathers
CW2442 Shell dish – green tail feathers
CW2443 Vase – pink tail feathers
CW2444 Vase – pink/yellow tail feathers
CW2445 Leaf dish – green tail feathers
CW2446 Leaf dish – yellow tail feathers
CW2447 Pitcher

CW2444

CW4106, CW4105

SHELL SWEETMEAT DISHES

Candies, nuts, and relishes were kept on hand to appeal to the eighteenth-century sweet tooth. These dishes are reproduced from antiques made between 1745 and 1759 at the Chelsea Porcelain Manufactory near London. The single white shell dish was painted in naturalistic enamel colors and used to hold salt or sweetmeats. The triple sweetmeat dish is reproduced from an unpainted dish made of three porcelain shells connected by an elaborate "rockwork and coral" handle.

CW4105 Single Shell
CW4106 Triple Shell

The "bowfat," or china closet, in the dining room at the Governor's Palace housed much of Lord Botetourt's decorative china and glassware, including "56 pieces ornamental china" for mantel decoration or elaborate dessert tables.

Visitors to Colonial Williamsburg may see pewter objects such as spoons and buttons made in molds at the Geddy Foundry.

P E W T E R
IN THE EIGHTEENTH CENTURY

Pewter is a tin-rich alloy with small amounts of copper, added for strength, bismuth and antimony for luster. These both harden the metal and enhance its working qualities. Owing to its low melting point, pewter is usually cast in permanent molds, most often of brass or bronze. The fact that pewter is cast, rather than wrought from sheet like silver, contributes to its appealing directness of form and ornament. Unlike silver with its surface brilliance, pewter is admired for depth and softness of color.

Since we rarely eat and drink from pewter vessels today, it is difficult for us to understand how common pewter was in English and American daily life of the seventeenth and eighteenth centuries. That was the great age of pewter, when the craft flourished and produced a remarkable range of goods for home and tavern as well as for religious and public institutions. Even though few pewterers can be documented in the South, in contrast to the North, pewter was no less widely used in the Chesapeake; there was simply a greater reliance on imported English wares. Here, as elsewhere, even those of modest means owned pewter including plates and dishes, basins and spoons, and more specialized forms such as tankards, teapots, and even soup tureens.

Immense quantities of pewter were shipped from English ports to America, where demand greatly outstripped local production. These exports mounted steadily so that by the 1760s more than 300 tons of pewter articles were shipped annually. This is the equivalent of almost 1,000,000 eight-inch plates or 300,000 quart mugs. By the last quarter of the century, pewter was increasingly replaced by less expensive and more fashionable ceramics.

— JOHN D. DAVIS
Senior Curator, Curator of Metalwork

PEWTER COFFEE SERVICE

Exotic coffee was drunk primarily in coffeehouses when first introduced in the mid-1600s. Eighteenth-century Virginians enjoyed coffee with breakfast and dinner, but kept to tea in the afternoon. This graceful coffeepot is adapted from a silver coffeepot made by London goldsmith Peter Archambo, Sr., in 1734-1735 and features a rosewood handle, tapered body, and 26-ounce capacity. The cream pitcher features a scalloped lip and fanciful handle reproduced from an English antique made during the last half of the eighteenth century. The gracefully rounded sugar bowl is an adaptation, patterned after the creamer.

CW86   Pewter Coffeepot
CW91   Pewter Cream Pitcher
CW92   Pewter Sugar

HEART BOX

This lovely container is reproduced in cast pewter and polished brass from an antique tobacco box. Craftsmen produced lidded storage jars and boxes in a range of materials. The classic style of this piece and its use of two metals are unusual. CW107

For a special gift, many of our pewter pieces may be engraved. Please refer to the ordering and services section for more information.

CW107

Left to right: CW91, CW86, CW92

Clockwise from left: CW80, CW180, CW79, CW81, CW82

Left to right front row: CW180, CW83, CW84, CW80; back row: CW59, CW12, CW76, CW79

PEWTER TEAPOT/COFFEEPOT

These elegant pewter tea- and coffeepots with rosewood handles are adaptations of an eighteenth-century original attributed to the London shop of Samuel Ellis. They are slightly larger than the original. Perhaps more than any other custom of the times, the storing, brewing, and serving of tea stimulated the development and flow of specialized consumer goods to accommodate the increased consumption of coffee and tea, especially at home.

CW180   Teapot – 28 oz.
CW80   Coffeepot – 40 oz.

PEWTER DISH

The original of this 13⅞″ reproduction was made in the London shop of Thomas King between 1689 and 1694. Flat pewter wares such as this were called "sadware." They were cast in many sizes and owned by many households. The multiple-reeded design of this dish is typical of its period but an unusual survival in a dish of this size. Diameter 13⅞″. CW79

CW83, CW84

PEWTER CREAM PITCHER AND SUGAR BOWL

Based on an antique circa 1740-1780, these cream pots have been reproduced in the original size and adapted in a smaller size. The pewter sugar bowls are based on the cream pot design. All feature pad feet, flared rim, and double-scroll legs and handle.

CW81   Cream Pitcher small
CW83   Cream Pitcher large
CW82   Sugar Bowl 3″
CW84   Sugar Bowl 4″

Connoisseurs of seventeenth- and eighteenth-century pewter may study Colonial Williamsburg's fine collection in the metals study gallery at the DeWitt Wallace Decorative Arts Gallery.

PEWTER STRAWBERRY DISH

This shallow dish with its fluted rim was reproduced from an English antique circa 1710-1740. This form of dish was fashioned originally out of silver. It was developed by eighteenth-century London silversmiths as a dessert dish. In Virginia, this dish might have made its appearance with tea or during one of the colonists' multi-course dinners. Diameter 5″. CW4

CW4

RALEIGH TAVERN SPOON

The original of this rugged but handsomely balanced silverplate spoon was found near the site of Williamsburg's Raleigh Tavern. During the eighteenth century, this tavern was the scene of auctions, lectures, balls, receptions, games of chance, good-fellowship, and heated political discussion. In 1783, it hosted the celebration of the end of the Revolution and the Treaty of Paris. In 1859, the tavern burned to its foundation. During its reconstruction between 1928-1930, the original spoon was discovered.

J30   Spoon
J31   Set of six spoons

J30

DRESSING SPOON

The original of this large bowled, long handled spoon was used by colonists for a variety of uses in the preparation and serving of food. Today, the reproduction makes an attractive dressing spoon for festive occasions. 13″ long. CW14

CW14

PEWTER PORRINGERS

The term "porringer" came into use in the sixteenth century. It may have been derived from the French *potager*, to cook in a pot. Porringers were all-purpose dishes in England and colonial America. In the seventeenth and eighteenth centuries, a man may have started the day eating porridge from an English-made eared dish such as these, later enjoyed soup or stew, then imbibed beer, wine, or cider from it.

CW15   Pewter Porringer 4¼″
CW16   Pewter Porringer 3¼″

CW15

CW16

Clockwise from left: CW10, CW7, CW5, CW54

PEWTER BOWLS

These bowls are adapted from a 5½″ pewter example in the Colonial Williamsburg collection. The pewter used in Williamsburg was imported primarily from England and was prized by the eighteenth-century housewife. She scoured it with sand and straw to keep it clean and shining. Today's lead-free pewter needs only to be washed and thoroughly dried to retain its shine.

CW5   Pewter Bowl 7¼″
CW7   Pewter Bowl 11″
CW10   Pewter Bowl 5½″

LARGE PEWTER STRAWBERRY DISH

This reproduction of an eighteenth-century antique features a shallow depth and scalloped rim. It was developed by English silversmiths in a period when multi-course meals made it desirable to have specialized serving pieces. This form was used for desserts. Diameter 11″. CW54

CW2

CW99

SCROLL-HANDLED PEWTER CUP

An antique English mug is the original from which this pewter cup is reproduced. It demonstrates the graceful S-curve often seen in furniture of the late baroque period. This straight-sided design, with its generous capacity and comfortable strap handle, would have been popular as a vessel for cider, punch, syllabub, or shrub. 6 oz. CW2

PEWTER CASTER

The practice of casting or sprinkling sugar on food using a large caster came into being in Europe during the seventeenth century. This pewter caster is reproduced from an English original. Height 7". CW99

PEWTER HUMIDORS

Tobacco was Virginia's major cash crop in the eighteenth century. English merchant ships lined the wharves of rivers throughout the tidewater region, waiting to load tobacco into their holds from nearby plantations. In return, they exchanged the English goods coveted by the colonists. Among those goods were tobacco jars and boxes such as these. The large size is reproduced from an English original; the smaller size is an adaptation.
CW93   Small Humidor 6"
CW94   Large Humidor 7¼"

For a special gift, many of our pewter pieces may be engraved. Please refer to the ordering and services section for more information.

CW94

CW93

Left to right: CW88, CW12, CW76, CW59, CW3

PEWTER TRAY

This pewter tray is adapted from one piece in a set of miniatures believed to have been made on the Continent. These miniatures served mainly as toys.
Diameter 10½″.   CW12

PEWTER PLATES

Pewter plates, dishes, mugs, tankards, and other everyday tableware were coveted in America long after earthenware had displaced pewter in England. Some English pewterers maintained their livelihood for several decades by manufacturing pewter tableware for export to the former colonies.
CW59   Plate 11″
CW76   Plate 5¼″

PEWTER BOWL AND BEAKER

This narrow-brimmed, flat-bottomed bowl is reproduced from a Boston original made by Thomas Badger circa 1800. Known as a "bason," this design was made in many sizes. The original of this reproduction beaker was made in Holland in several sizes as drinking vessels.
CW3   Pewter Bowl 8″
CW88   Pewter Beaker 8¼″

Clockwise from top left: CW97, CW96, CW98, CW90

PEWTER SALT AND PEPPER SHAKERS

Starting in the seventeenth century, casters were used to cast or sprinkle sugar, pepper, and other condiments. These handsome adaptations have been made in a smaller size more appropriate for modern use as salt and pepper shakers. Height 5⅛″.
CW96   Salt Shaker
CW97   Pepper Shaker

PEWTER OPEN SALT AND SPOON

Small dishes of salt appeared on tables during the seventeenth century. The largest and most ornate was placed before the most honored guest. Other simpler salts were placed around the table. This open pewter salt and the pewter spoon that can accompany it are reproduced from an eighteenth-century antique.
CW98   Pewter Open Salt
Diameter 2¾″
CW90   Pewter Salt Spoon
Length 3″

DECORATIVE
ACCESSORIES IN THE EIGHTEENTH CENTURY

In the eighteenth century a dramatic expansion in the variety and availability of specialized goods occurred. Household inventories and the advertisements of proliferating stores and specialty shops, as well as surviving objects, illustrate the burgeoning demand by growing numbers of affluent consumers for an ever-greater range of fashionable goods. Matters of taste and refinement were no longer limited just to the upper levels of society, but increasingly became middle-class concerns and choices as well.

Polite activities, especially tea drinking and dining, were conspicuous. By the early decades of the eighteenth century these had become organized occasions for genteel social interaction and expression. This greatly affected the production of silversmiths, pewterers, potters, and cabinetmakers.

Many decorative accessories used in Virginia and elsewhere in the colonies, whether brass candlesticks and fire tools, delft and creamware plates and dishes, teapots and teacups, crystal wine glasses and decanters, and mahogany tea chests and wall brackets, came from England. By the end of the eighteenth century, in response to these enormous demands, many trades involved had become industries with efficient means of large-scale production, marketing, and distribution.

— JOHN D. DAVIS

John D. Davis, *senior curator and curator of metalwork, wrote* English Silver at Williamsburg. *A similar catalog of the pewter in the collection is in progress.*

A tavern keeper could supply his guests with a number of comforting amenities, including mugs of beer or cider, candles, gaming equipment, pipes, and hearty meals. The Raleigh catered to the gentry, and so had relatively elegant furnishings.

Left to right: C5, C26, C27, C40, C29

EIGHTEENTH-CENTURY
DELFT

One of the most popular ceramic wares in the British colonies in America was a tin-glazed earthenware that was referred to as delft and often spelled *delph* or *delf*. The name for the ware was due to the strong influence of potters from Holland who came to England to carry on their trade. Although basically Dutch, the ware soon began to acquire a definite English flavor in both form and decoration. Western landscapes and flowers were mingled with designs from the Orient. The Chinese blue and white porcelain was both copied exactly and adapted or altered to fit the westerners' interests or needs. Placing Oriental decoration on European forms did not bother them at all. Even mixing eastern and western decoration on the piece did not seem odd as it might to twentieth-century purists. One must not think only of blue and white when considering delft, for other colors were very much a part of the ware. Purple from manganese, green from copper, yellow from antimony, and red from iron were used to decorate a ware as colorful as European porcelain.

Delft continued to be made in England throughout the eighteenth century. Its heavier body was more suited to the styles of the earlier part of the century, however, so by 1800 production had all but ceased.

— JOHN C. AUSTIN
Senior Curator
Curator of Ceramics and Glass

DELFT BRICKS AND JARDINIÈRE

The delft jardinière, pictured above left, is reproduced from a pair of English flower holders made about 1750. Brick-shaped flower containers were a mid-eighteenth-century invention of English delftware potters. The polychrome brick to the right of the jardinière is reproduced from a pair of antiques made in Bristol. The blue delft brick is reproduced from an antique English flower container made during the second quarter of the eighteenth century and features the popular "mimosa" motif. The small "Chinese" brick, based on an original made in Bristol about 1740, is modeled with bracket feet and decorated to resemble the highly fashionable and costly Chinese porcelains of the period. The round brick is reproduced from an original made in London about 1700.

C5   Delft Jardinière - Height 4¼"; Width 5" top, 4¼" bottom
C26 Small "Chinese" Brick - Height 2½"; Length 4⅞"
C27 Polychrome Brick - Height 3½"; Length 6"
C40 Round Brick - Height 2½"; Diameter 6"
C29 Blue Delft Brick - Height 3¾"; Length 6¼"

Delft Wallpockets

Wallpockets were used as containers for everlastings, garden flowers and foliage grown for their color, then dried and arranged in bouquets that lasted throughout the winter. The originals of these reproduction English wall vases were made circa 1750 at a pottery in London, England, an important center for the manufacture of delft. The blue decoration represents typical English attempts to duplicate or adapt Oriental designs. Height 8″.

C36 Boy with Hat
C37 Girl

Polychrome Delft Pitcher

This colorful design is adapted in delft from an eighteenth-century English salt-glazed stoneware original made in Staffordshire, England, about 1750-1760. It probably was used for beer or ale. Its sturdy barrel shape and comfortable loop handle are enhanced by an outward-pressing handle terminal and a triangular spout embellished with a tiny motif that complements the patterned floral sprays. Height 6¼″; Capacity 1¼ qts. C33

C33

Delft Vase

The original of this vase probably was made in London, England, about 1730. As with many other household items, delft was popular in Virginia and other colonies after it had passed out of fashion in England. Large quantities of shards have been found at every eighteenth-century excavation site in Williamsburg. Height 5½″. C32

Delft Urn

The original of this reproduction urn is attributed to a pottery in London, England, circa 1730 and featured a glaze with a distinctive bluish tint. This reproduction piece demonstrates the classic urn shape. Decorative elements and narrow fillets, or stripes, follow its contours. Height 6″. C30

C36, C37

C32, C30

C52

Delft Oval Dish

The original of this oval dish was made in London, England, during the late seventeenth century and probably was used for potted meat. This process involved preserving or pickling the meat with spices, salt, vinegar, or other ingredients. Today this bowl might be used to serve nuts or hold a small plant. Height 3¼″; Length 7″. C52

C56-1 Home by the Sea

C56-2 Well by the Sea

C56-7 Farm by the Sea

C56-8 Bridge by the Sea

C56-3 Harbor by the Sea

C56-4 Tree by the Sea

Shown clockwise from left: C82, C49, C10, C48, C53, and C51

DELFT WINE BOTTLE

The original of this unusually shaped reproduction earthenware bottle was made in England about 1760. It was used as a water bottle for washing. C82

LARGE DELFT VASE

The London original of this reproduction vase was made circa 1740, and may have been used in eighteenth-century Williamsburg. Height 10¼". C49

DELFT PLATE

The original fragments of this plate were excavated in Williamsburg. Diameter 10¼". C10

Because delft tiles were excavated on the site of the Governor's Palace, they were incorporated into the reconstructed building, as seen in the chamber over the dining room.

DELFT CASTER

Casters were introduced into England from France in the seventeenth century. Early casters were made of silver or pewter and often were called muffineers. Larger casters were used for sugar and smaller ones were for pepper and mustard. This is a reproduction of an eighteenth-century Dutch delft caster. Height 6⅜"; Diameter 3". C53

DELFT PITCHER

The original of this reproduction is from Liverpool, England, circa 1760. The large lip spout, substantial strap loop handle, and sturdy footring make this pear-shaped jug easy to use. Height 9¼"; Capacity 2 qts. C48

C56-9   House by the Sea

C56-10   Sweep by the Sea

C56-11   Factory by the Sea

C56-12   Mill by the Sea

C56-5   Tower by the Sea

C56-6   Castle by the Sea

Left to right: C55, C47, C31 and C41

Delft Porringer

Porringers were popular for individual servings of porridge, soups, and stews in the seventeenth and eighteenth centuries. These bowl-like vessels also were suited for feeding children. This reproduction is based on an eighteenth-century delft original made in London, England, about 1740. It features the single flat handle characteristic of English designs as opposed to its two-handled Dutch counterpart. Height 2⅛"; Diameter 5½". C51

Delft Tiles

"Home by the Sea" was reproduced from an eighteenth-century tile found during archaeological excavations of the Governor's Palace grounds. It was replaced in a fireplace in the reconstructed building along with related tiles of the same period. From this group, eleven other tiles have been reproduced. 5¼" square.

Delft Cream Jug

This is an adaptation of a smaller jug made in Liverpool, England, circa 1760. The delicate process of decorating this pitcher involves hand painting the design directly onto unfired tin enamel, making retouching impossible. Height 4½". C31

Delft Sweetmeat Trays

The eighteenth-century fondness for sweetmeats, as confections then were called, required that a thoughtful hostess have a variety of small serving dishes on hand. These reproductions are based on originals from Liverpool, England, circa 1750.
C47   Shell-shaped Sweetmeat Tray - Width 3¾".
C55   Triangular-shaped Sweetmeat Tray - Side length 4¾".

Delft Polychrome Saucer

This saucer is reproduced from a small eighteenth-century English plate excavated at the site of the Prentis House on Duke of Gloucester Street. Diameter 4½". C41

Delft Tobacco Jars

Jars such as these may have been used by a colonial storekeeper to store his patrons' favorite tobacco blends. This series of jars has been reproduced with the original "Carolina" inscription and adapted to bear the name of each of the other original colonies. The brass top, a modern addition for more practical storage, can be purchased separately. Height 10⅜".
C60 Carolina   C76 Virginia   C91 Massachusetts

Left to right: C-60, C-76, C-91

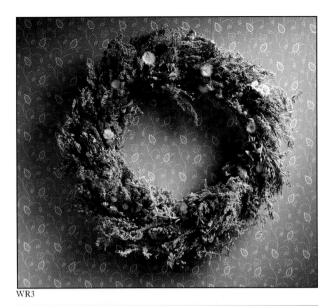

WR3

"Secret gardens" are one of the great appeals of Williamsburg at any season.

WFA5

WREATHS AND DRIED FLOWERS

Flowers were popular in many forms during the eighteenth century, including dried flowers or "everlastings." These lovely dried flower products draw on the eighteenth-century art of flower drying to create a variety of forms for decorating walls, doors, tabletops, or windows.

WR1 Dried Flower Wreath — small
WR2 Dried Flower Wreath — medium
WR3 Dried Flower Wreath — large
WFA5 Flower Covered Grapevine Wreath — small 9½"
WFA3 Flower Covered Grapevine Wreath — large 13"

POSY HOLDER

Flowers often were picked at their peak, carefully dried to preserve their form and color, then displayed in a vase such as this fanciful design reproduced from an eighteenth-century English flower container. This type of vase also may have held fresh cut flowers. The same "five finger" design appears in a pattern book first issued by Leeds Pottery in Yorkshire, makers of fine cream colored earthenware in 1774. Height 7¾".

POSY HOLDER

1070

M31

SPIKE BOOTSCRAPER

By 1732, four iron mines and blast furnaces were operating in colonial Virginia. Despite Parliament's Iron Act of 1750, smiths continued to forge farm tools and ironwork, including the original of this sturdy bootscraper. It offers a quick way to clean shoes that is as practical today as it was in the eighteenth century. Height 7"; Length 10". 1070

CW1609

JACK RACK

In the late eighteenth century, brass jack racks were used in colonial kitchens to suspend pots and kettles over the fire. This handsome polished brass example features an intricately pierced arm, making it an attractive support for plants or other items. Height 7¼"; Length 11". CW1609

CW23-9B

BIRD BOTTLE

This unusual birdhouse, also known as a martin pot, is based on an original excavated from the James Geddy House yard in Williamsburg. It was usually hooked under the eaves of a building or hung from a tree to encourage purple martins and other insect-eating birds to nest inside it. Length 8¾". M31

SUNDIAL

Horizontal sundials were used to measure daylight hours. This distinctive sundial is adapted from an original made in the early 1700s by W. Collier of London, England, and is available in polished brass or cast-iron verdigris. Diameter 11¾".
CW23-9B   Polished brass sundial
CW23-9CI/V   Cast-iron verdigris sundial

CW23-9CI/V

Left to right front row: CW7-33, CW6-44, CW78; back row: CW8-25, Z5007, CW12-14

QUEEN ANNE BOOKENDS

These solid brass bookends are interpreted from an illustration in *A New Book of Cyphers* by Samuel Sympson, published in London about 1750. This particular cipher with its intertwined "AR" denoting "Anna Regina" was the royal monogram of England's Queen

Anne. She began her twelve-year reign in 1702, three years after Williamsburg was selected as the capital of the Virginia colony.
Height 5⅞". CW8-25

HELMET INKSTAND

Well-formed handwriting was a mark of gentility and education in the eighteenth century. A gentleman practiced calligraphy to perfect his handwriting. One of the tools he may have used is the original of this reproduction inkstand. Diameter 5". CW78

Z5225 FOLK ART
CHRISTMAS TREE
Diameter 1⅝"

Z5007 BLUE FLOWERS
Diameter 1⅛"

Z5143 MAY THE
RIGHTS OF MAN
1½" x 1⅔"

Z5008 GRAPES
Diameter 1⅛"

Z5009 MR. PUNCH
Diameter 1½"

Z5147 CAT
1½" x 1¼"

GOVERNOR'S PALACE KEY PAPERWEIGHT

The Palace of England's largest and most prosperous colony was the official residence of seven royal governors between 1715 and 1775. It was an outpost of British taste and style as well as the center of Virginia's social and political life. This brass paperweight is reproduced from one of the keys to the Governor's Palace. Length 8″. CW6-44

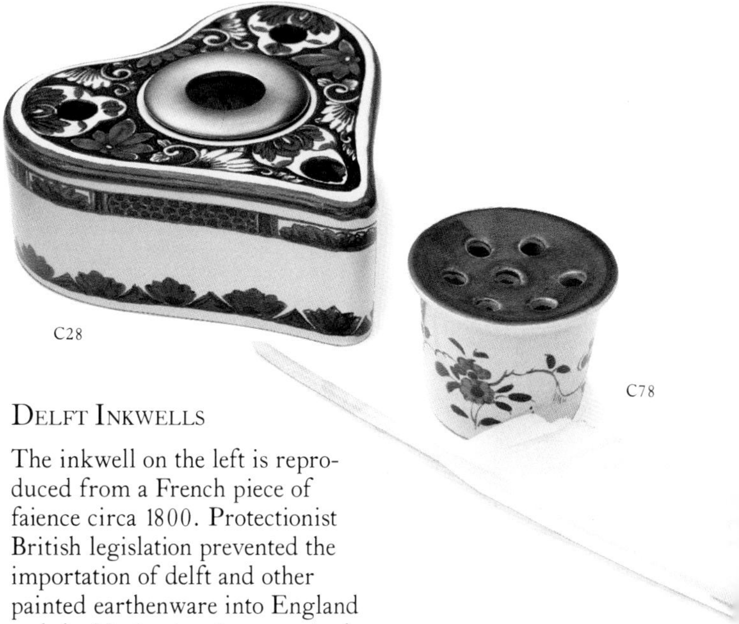

BRASS BOX

In the eighteenth century, a gentlemen might have used a special box such as this for carrying tobacco or snuff. The original of this polished brass interpretive box was made in London by Edward Cornock in 1723-1724. It is ideal for holding small dresser or vanity items, and may be personalized by engraving. Diameter 3″ x 4″.
CW7-32   Plain
CW7-33   Engraved

CW7-33

BRASS FRAMES AND MIRROR

In the late seventeenth century, shoe buckles were made of many metals and shapes. They often were engraved or inset with stones, indicating the status of the wearer. The frames are adapted from a patterned buckle and made of solid brass. The mirror has an easel back allowing vertical or horizontal use.
CW14-10   Mirror; 10¼″ x 12¼″
CW12-14   For 3″ x 5″ photo; 4½″ x 6½″
CW12-15   For 5″ x 7″ photo; 7¼″ x 9¼″
CW12-16   For 8″ x 10″ photo; 10¼″ x 12¼″

ENAMEL BOXES

During the seventeenth and eighteenth centuries, ladies indulged in wearing fashionable face patches made of black silk and often cut into fanciful shapes. Their popularity led craftsmen to make containers to store these beauty spots. English enamels may be the most charming of all these containers. They often were embellished with mottoes, poems, or sayings of topical interest. These particular boxes are adapted, interpreted, and made in the original manner of those crafted in England by Crummles & Co.

C28

C78

DELFT INKWELLS

The inkwell on the left is reproduced from a French piece of faience circa 1800. Protectionist British legislation prevented the importation of delft and other painted earthenware into England and the Navigation Acts required that all goods to the colonies be carried on English ships, so during the eighteenth century, most delft imported into the colonies was made in England.
C28   Delft Heart Inkwell — Height 1⅞″; Width 4⅞″
C78   Delft Quill Holder — Diameter 2⅜″; Height 1⅞″

CW12-15, CW14-10

Z5150 BLUE BOX,
THIS TRIFLE THO SMALL
1⅞″ x 1¼″

Z5006 WORCESTER PLATE
2½″ x 1¼″

Z5144 PINK BOX,
TRIFLING IS MY PRESENT
1⅞″ x 1¼″

Z5142 GOVERNOR'S PALACE
2⅛″ x 1¼″

Z5151 CHRISTMAS BOX,
A PRESENT
Diameter 1⅝″

Shown clockwise from left: M22-642, M53-708, M59-601, M25-601

Shown clockwise from left: C702, C701, C703, C704

Shown clockwise from bottom: QUILT, THEOREM and SHIPS

FOLK ART ADDRESS BOOK

CATESBY ADDRESS BOOK

FOLK ART ADDRESS BOOK

During the late 1920s, Abby Aldrich Rockefeller began collecting folk art, long before most people realized its aesthetic and cultural value. This lovely hard cover address book is illustrated with forty color photographs of objects and portraits from the Abby Aldrich Rockefeller Folk Art Center.

CATESBY ADDRESS BOOK

This beautifully illustrated address book features twenty color prints from Mark Catesby's *Natural History of Carolina, Florida and the Bahama Islands* published in 1731 and 1743. It has a fabric covering and imprinted spine.

INVITATIONS

These gracious invitations are based on a variety of eighteenth-century decorative motifs. Worcester Floral is derived from the design on a Worcester porcelain vase and leaf dish. Flowered Silk Coverlet is interpreted from a bed counterpane made in China for export. Chinese Peony is based on a rare hand-painted wallpaper made in China and featuring the peony, symbolizing spring.

M22-642   Worcester Floral Invitations
M53-708   Chinese Peony Invitations
M59-601   Flowered Silk Coverlet Informal Notes
M25-601   Flowered Silk Coverlet Invitations

EMBOSSED NOTECARDS

These tastefully designed cards were inspired by eighteenth-century decorative motifs. The Pineapple is taken from a wallpaper fragment. The Shell design is inspired by an intricately sculpted ceramic bowl made about 1785. The Fruit Basket is taken from an English creamware bowl made between 1780 and 1800. The Butterfly Floral is inspired by the beautiful Chelsea porcelain botanical designs.

C702   Pineapple
C701   Shell
C703   Fruit Basket
C704   Butterfly Floral

Clockwise from bottom left: P22-42, G2-42, G92-42, A1-42, CS-742, CT-742

NOTECARDS

Nineteenth-century decorative motifs are the inspiration for these museum quality notecards. The Baltimore Album Quilt pattern is derived from a remarkable Baltimore quilt, circa 1850, depicting three Baltimore landmarks and the capitol at Washington, D. C. The four Theorem designs are inspired by nineteenth-century theorem paintings from between 1826 and 1840. The Ships designs come from four American oil-on-canvas paintings made between 1805 and 1852. The Theorem and Ships originals are all in the Abby Aldrich Rockefeller Folk Art Center collection.

Quilt
Theorem
Ships

WORCESTER FLORAL

The basis for this lovely design is found on a Worcester porcelain vase and leaf dish in the Colonial Williamsburg collection. This pattern was particularly long-lived compared with many of the more faddish eighteenth-century porcelain designs.

P22-42   Libromount Photo Album
G2-42   Guest Book
G92-42   Personal Journal
A1-42   Address Book
CS-742   Letter Paper
CT-742   Thank You Notes

EIGHTEENTH-CENTURY WOODENWARE

The production of fine woodenware for domestic utensils and personal accessories has a long British tradition. Refined examples often exhibit the same specialized skills in their construction and decoration as sophisticated furniture.

— JOHN D. DAVIS
Senior Curator
Curator of Metalwork

Thomas Chippendale's influential pattern book The Gentleman and Cabinet-Maker's Director *provided cabinetmakers and patrons with designs not only for furniture but also accessory items such as tea chests.*

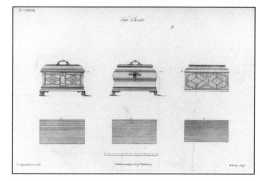

WOODEN BOXES

Tea was first introduced into England from the Orient during the middle of the seventeenth century. Within a century, tea drinking became an integral part of English and colonial culture. Anxious for revenue, Parliament imposed a Tea Tax on the colonies in 1773. The colonists' response was the Boston Tea Party and subsequent boycott of tea.

Tea chests, a fixture in more affluent English and colonial homes, were crafted by artisans of considerable skill. This reproduction of an octagonal tea chest from an antique circa 1740-1760 requires hand-fitting more than 25 separate pieces of mahogany. This chest can serve as a jewel box when ordered with a velvet lining.

CW101   Octagonal
Tea Chest —
Height 4¾″;
Diameter 6¼″
CW102   Oblong
Tea Chest —
Height 6″;
Length 10″;
Depth 6″
CW103   Oblong
Jewel Box —
Height 6″;
Length 10″;
Depth 6″

CW101

CW102, CW103

MAHOGANY MIRROR AND WALL BRACKET

Small looking glasses such as this often were used for shaving or dressing. This reproduction, based on a rococo English original made about 1770, features the highly arched scrolled crest and graceful symmetry of the original. The original of this wall bracket was made about 1760 in England and probably held a candlestick, ornamental ceramics, or a small shelf clock. The support is in the style of a late baroque cabriole leg.

CW104   Mahogany Mirror - Overall
size 9½″ x 19½″
CW109   Mahogany Wall Bracket -
Height 9″; Width 12½″;
Depth 8″

SPOON RACK

The spoon rack made its appearance in England during the reign of Elizabeth I and was solely utilitarian. This adaptation of a late eighteenth-century oak spoon rack is as decorative as it is useful. It is made of solid mahogany, hand-fitted, and features a simple scallop-and-heart motif. Height 23″; Width 12½″; Depth 5⅜″. CW131

QUEEN ANNE TRAY

This hand-carved, solid mahogany reproduction is based on an original made in England circa 1730-1770. Trays such as this appear in the inventory of Lord Botetourt, royal governor of the Virginia colony. It features indented corners and bracket feet similar to those of silver trays from this period. Height 1¼″; Length 18³⁄₁₆″; Width 13″. CW125

GAMING BOARD

This meticulously hand-fitted reproduction of an eighteenth-century original features parquetry, the technique of using geometric shapes of contrasting woods to make various designs. Inveterate gamblers and gamesters, colonial Virginians enjoyed their games in numerous popular taverns. 17¼″ square. CW127; checkers also available.

CW131

CW104, CW109

CW125

CW127

TAVERNWARE, pages 300-301; CANDLESTICK, page 225; PITCHER, page 275; MUG, page 309.

TAVERN COASTERS

TAVERN NAPKINS

TAVERN NAPKINS

In eighteenth-century Williamsburg, a number of taverns provided hospitality to the traveling public. These napkins interpret various tavern signs found throughout the town. Box of 200. 51-150

TAVERN COASTERS

In 1766, Josiah Chowning advertised his tavern's opening in the *Virginia Gazette* by promising that "all who please to favor me with their custom may depend on the best of entertainment for themselves, servants, and horses, and good pasturage." These coasters interpret the sign hanging outside of Chowning's Tavern, as well as those of Christiana Campbell's, King's Arms, and Shields. 4⅛" square. 127266

TAVERN KITCHEN TOWELS

TAVERN KITCHEN TOWELS

In the eighteenth century, tavern kitchens were busy places as tavern keepers were expected to provide patrons with a choice of meat, fish, fruits, and vegetables in season as well as a choice of beverages. These kitchen towels are interpreted from four brightly colored tavern signs in Williamsburg. Made of 100 percent linen, each measures 27″ x 17″.

03-575 Shields Tavern
03-572 Chowning's Tavern
03-574 King's Arms Tavern
03-573 Christiana Campbell's Tavern

TAVERN SIGNS

These interpretations of signs seen in taverns in the Historic Area of Williamsburg were inspired by William Hogarth's depiction of tavern signs in eighteenth-century prints. These signs promised a place of food and rest for gentlemen, servants, and horses. Ladies seldom traveled but, if they did, usually stayed with friends or in a private boardinghouse. 24½″ x 32½″.

TAVERN SIGNS

TAVERN DINNER MATS

Tavern keepers usually were people of consequence during the eighteenth century. They hosted guests, were conversant with all matters of moment, and knew when to keep counsel or keep silent. They also provided ample food and refreshment to weary travelers. These tavern placemats are interpreted from signs that may have hung outside several such establishments in Williamsburg. These dinner mats are acrylic-finished for easy cleaning and measure 16″ x 12″.

Visual symbols, for those who could not read, accompanied many shop and tavern signs.

TAVERN DINNER MATS

THEOREM DINNER PLACEMATS

THEOREM COASTERS

THEOREM TABLE
ACCESSORIES

These delicately patterned placemats and coasters are interpreted from colorful paintings stenciled during the 1820s and 1830s. Cut-outs were laid over fabric or paper and filled with painted color. The Abby Aldrich Rockefeller Folk Art Center in Williamsburg houses a large collection of these nineteenth-century paintings.

Set of 6 Coasters with green border, 4⅛″ square.

Set of 4 Dinner Placemats with green border, 15¾″ x 11¾″.

SCENES OF WILLIAMSBURG COASTERS

SCENES OF WILLIAMSBURG DINNER PLACEMATS, WITH LUNCHEON PLACEMAT ON TOP

SCENES OF
WILLIAMSBURG TABLE
ACCESSORIES

As the capital of the Virginia colony for eighty-one years, Williamsburg was the political, economic, and cultural center of a vast and prosperous English holding. The Capitol, Governor's Palace, Wren Building, and Raleigh Tavern each have a special history in the evolution of the colony into a state.

Set of 6 Coasters with claret border, 4⅛″ square.

Set of 4 Dinner Placemats with claret border, 16″ x 12″.

Set of 4 Luncheon Placemats with claret border, 12″ x 9″.

Trivet with claret border, 8½″ x 7½″.

DINNER PLACEMAT

LUNCHEON PLACEMAT

COASTER

FURBER FLORAL TABLE ACCESSORIES

These handsome table accessories are interpreted from a series of prints designed by Peter Casteels, engraved by Henry Fletcher, and published by Robert Furber about 1730. Originally published as a catalog, the illustrations quickly became popular for their decorative value. The floral arrangements of these placemats and coasters have been altered to fit a horizontal format. They are available with different colored borders.

Set of 6 Coasters with cream or black border, 4⅛" square.
Set of 6 Luncheon Placemats with cream or black border, 12" x 9".
Set of 4 Dinner Placemats with cream or black border, 16" x 12".
The above are available with a green border by special order.

FURBER FLORAL DINNER PLACEMATS

CHECKED GREEN

CHECKED RED

CHECKED BLUE

CHECKED SAGE

CW 10-10

BRASS AND IRON TRIVETS

This series of sandcast and hand-finished interpretive trivets exemplifies the propensity of well-to-do eighteenth-century householders for using their monograms, also known as a cipher, to mark their most important possessions. The King George trivet with its GR for Georgius Rex and numeral 2, the Queen Anne trivet with its AR for Anna Regina, the royal monogram of the William and Mary trivet, the CW Colonial Williamsburg trivet, the armorial emblem of the King's Arms Tavern on the King's Arms trivet, and the William Rex with a WR for William III all illustrate designs of monograms and coats of arms. The *Carter's Grove*™ Trivet represents a stylized flower of the tobacco plant, the "Imperial Weed" on which the tidewater Virginia economy was built in the eighteenth century.

CW10-10   Queene Anne Trivet in brass, iron — 9″ × 10½″.

CW10-47   *Carter's Grove*™ Trivet in brass only — Diameter 5¾″.

CW10-9   King George Trivet in brass only — 4″ x 5″.

CW10-14   Colonial Williamsburg Trivet in bronze, brass, iron — Diameter 6″.

CW10-11   William and Mary Trivet in brass, iron — 6″ x 8″.

CW10-17   King's Arms Trivet in brass only — 5½″ x 6″.

CW10-50   William Rex Trivet in brass, iron — 7½″ x 6″.

™ Identifies trademark of The Colonial Williamsburg Foundation

CHECKED LINENS

These linens were inspired by a linen seat cushion in the Colonial Williamsburg Foundation textile collection. In the colonies, these indigo, red, or green and white checked slipcovers were used all year to prevent sunlight, dust, and dirt from damaging furniture. This modern interpretation, using a linen-cotton blend, will launder to a pleasant softness and absorbency. 18¼″ x 28″.

08-901   Checked red
08-902   Checked blue
08-903   Checked green
08-904   Checked sage

CW 10-47

CW 10-9

GERMAN TOY VILLAGE

These eight tiny buildings are reproduced from a set of hand-carved toys made in Germany in the mid- to late nineteenth century. The German wooden toy tradition originated when coal miners took up woodworking to fill their spare winter hours. They started specializing in toymaking, forming the basis of a network of village craftsmen who later expanded into international sales. Toys such as this were ordered through colorful catalogs and imported extensively into America during the 1800s. This set includes a storage box. Height 1¼″ to 4″.

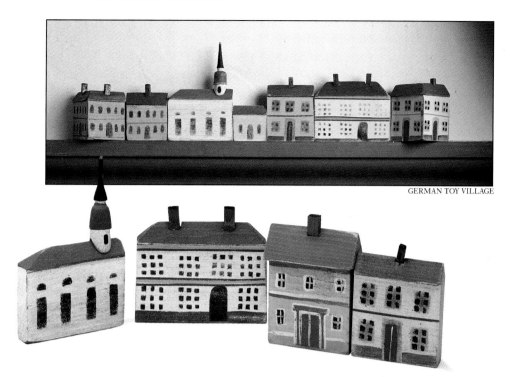
GERMAN TOY VILLAGE

"CHANTICLEER" LINENS

The jacquard damask border on these fingertip towels was inspired by a border tape probably made in Italy during the seventeenth century. It features tiny red roosters, known as "chanticleers" in Middle English, cross-stitched on an off-white background. 11¼″ x 16″.
Chanticleer Tea Towel — rose
Chanticleer Tea Towel — blue

"CHANTICLEER" LINENS

CW 10-14

CW 10-11

CW 10-17

CW 10-50

Left to right top row: 951-03, 954-03, 954-01, 956-03, 952-01, bottom row: 950-14, 958-01, 959-01, 954-03; 951-01, and 952-03.

"LIONS" TEA TOWEL

"VINES" AND "LION" TEA TOWELS

The graceful "vines" design is interpreted from a nineteenth-century blue-green wool and white cotton jacquard coverlet woven by John Klinhinz of Ohio. "Lion" is interpreted from a nineteenth-century natural cotton and red wool jacquard coverlet woven in 1839 by Harry Tyler of Jefferson County, New York, for Lucretia Ann Smith. Both interpretations are made of 100 percent cotton. 24″ x 31″.

Vines — blue
Vines — rose
Lion — blue
Lion — rose

SALT-GLAZED STONEWARE

Salt-glazed stoneware was created by throwing salt into a hot kiln during firing. The resulting sodium gas bonds with the stoneware to form a distinctive vitreous coating. This type of pottery was produced in large quantities during the nineteenth century. Shapes evolved into more straight-sided forms as technology and production progressed. Bird and floral motifs were familiar decorative designs. These particular designs were made in the nineteenth century and are part of the Abby Aldrich Rockefeller Folk Art Center collection.

REINDEER WEATHER VANE

The running or leaping deer was a popular and recurring design in nineteenth-century weather vanes, watercolors, frakturs, and calligraphic exercises. Like the original from which it is reproduced, this delightful design is structurally and imaginatively supported by thin iron bands soldered to its right side. Height 20¾″; length 32¼″.

1087   Weathervane
1088   Bracket

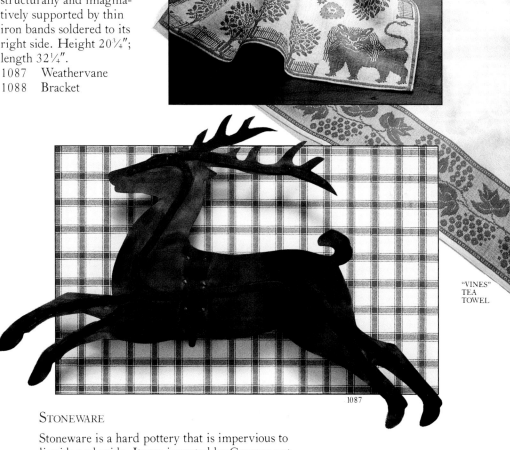

"VINES" TEA TOWEL

1087

	Height	Capacity
954-03 Large bird crock	8⅛″	1½ gallon
952-03 Medium bird crock	5¼″	1⅓ quart
951-03 Small bird crock	3¼″	½ pint
954-01 Large flower crock	8⅛″	1½ gallon
952-01 Medium flower crock	5¼″	1⅓ quart
951-01 Small flower crock	3¼″	½″ pint
958-01 Large flower pitcher	8¾″	2 quarts
959-01 Small flower pitcher	6¼″	scant pint
959-03 Small bird pitcher	6¼″	scant pint
956-03 Bluebird jar	10¼″	3½ quarts
950-14 Brownstone mug	7″	1 pint

STONEWARE

Stoneware is a hard pottery that is impervious to liquids and acids. It was invented by German potters in the fifteenth century and adopted by English potters three centuries later. These attractive stoneware serving dishes were inspired by fragments excavated in Williamsburg and Jamestown. Each features traditional incised and slip-cast techniques. The fern and honeysuckle footed trays are based on sweetmeat trays made in Staffordshire, England, about 1760. The star and fish molds are ovenproof versions of antiques.

C8   Fern tray — Length 6″
C9   Honeysuckle tray — Length 6½″
M15   Star mold — Height 1½″; Depth 3½″
M16   Fish mold — Length 5⅞″
M17   Fish Mold — Length 8¼″

Left to right: C9, M15, M16, and C8

Left to right: M36, M35, M5, M18, M25

SLIPWARE DISH

This handsome dish is reproduced in a fashion similar to the original. The clay is shaped over a domed mold, then decorated by trailing a pattern of slip, a mixture made from clay and water. A clear glaze is applied and the piece is kiln-fired.

M36   Zig-zag Slipware Dish — Diameter 7″
M35   Straight Slipware Dish — Diameter 7¼″

RECTANGULAR SLIPWARE DISH

This reproduction is based on an eighteenth-century comb-painted antique imported to the colonies from England. Dishes such as this were made of unfired clay, coated with a light colored slip, then patterned using a bristle, stick, or other pointed tool. Length 16¾″. M5

SLIPWARE JUG

The original of this pear-shaped earthenware jug was made in Devonshire, England, and is dated 1792. Like the antique, this reproduction features a red body, white slip, and yellow lead glaze. It also has a small lip spout, loop handle, and "1792" and the initials "EM" cut into the slip using a technique called "sgraffito." Height 5″. M30

M30

DOTWARE CANDLESTICK

The eighteenth-century original of this reproduction was excavated at the site of Anthony Hay's cabinetmaking shop in Williamsburg. This modestly priced but highly functional hand candlestick provided light to the bearer when carried down dark passages and staircases. Height 2½″; Diameter 4½″. M18

MARBLED SLIPWARE PIE PLATE

Copied from fragments excavated by archaeologists at Colonial Williamsburg, this colorful earthenware pie plate can be used as a serving dish. As with all slipware, it should not be exposed to prolonged high oven temperatures or the fine glaze may crack. Diameter 10¼″. M25

M35 Round Slipware Dish — Diameter 7¼″

M34 Oblong Slipware Dish — Length 6″; Diameter 5″

M6 Rectangular Slipware Dish — Diameter 8½″

M14 Rectangular Slipware Dish — Diameter 4½″

M27 Marbled Slipware Pie Plate — Diameter 5½″

M26 Marbled Slipware Pie Plate — Diameter 7½″

STONEWARE MUGS

Interpreted from eighteenth-century Rhenish fragments uncovered in Williamsburg, these mugs feature an incised cobalt blue design. These German mugs were made for export to England and her colonies where they were used to hold beer and ale.

M 11   Large Stoneware Mug — Height 5¾"; Capacity 36 oz.

M 11S   Medium Stoneware Mug — Height 4½"; Capacity 16 oz.

M 12   Child's Small Stoneware Mug — Height 3½"; Capacity 7 oz.

STONEWARE PRESERVES JAR

This handsome and functional jar is reproduced from an eighteenth-century German stoneware crock. Jars such as these appeared in pantries in colonial Virginia homes and taverns. They held pickled fruits and vegetables, compotes, and condiments. Height 5⅜". M 33

STONEWARE PAP BOAT

The unusual shape of this rare Staffordshire pottery reproduction is determined by its function: feeding infants or invalids soft, semi-liquid food. The bowl was filled with gruel or pablum that could be fed easily through the spout. Length 4". M 39

Colonists imported their ceramic wares from England, so there was no potter in eighteenth-century Williamsburg. Today's visitors, however, may better understand the potter's craft after studying this display on ceramic production in the "Patron and Tradesman" exhibit at the DeWitt Wallace Decorative Arts Gallery.

SCRATCH BLUE SALT AND PEPPER CASTERS

Inspired by an antique salt-glazed stoneware caster enameled with flowers, these pieces have been adapted with inscriptions. Scratch blue is an English form of ornamentation that evolved from the stoneware of the Rhineland.

M 19   Pepper Caster — Height 5"

M 20   Salt Caster — Height 5"

Left to right: M 11S, M 11, M 12, M 33, M 19, M 39, M 20

Shown left to right: CRANBERRY OHIO GRAPEVINE, DELFT GEOMETRIC CHECK, FOREST TYLER LION PILLOWS, CRANBERRY GEOMETRIC CHECK, NAVY PEACOCK, ROSE OHIO GRAPEVINE, and DELFT TYLER LION LAP BLANKETS

DELFT HOUSES

These diminutive delftware houses are handsomely detailed interpretations of buildings in the Historic Area of Colonial Williamsburg.

CWH3   King's Arms Barber Shop
CWH6   Brush-Everard House
CWH5   Pasteur & Galt Apothecary
CWH4   Davidson Shop
CWH1   Taliaferro-Cole Shop
CWH2   Nicolson Store

PAINTED LOOKING GLASS

During the colonial period in America, looking glasses were expensive and highly prized. Diminutive mirrors such as this one often were used for shaving or dressing. Reproduced from an original made in England about 1730-1770, this charming mirror is made by skilled woodworkers and is painted by hand. Height 13⅝"; Width 6¾".

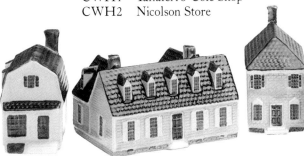

Left to right: CWH3, CWH6, CWH5, CWH4, CWH1, and CWH2

JACQUARD LAP BLANKETS AND PILLOWS

These boldly designed lap blankets are interpreted from three nineteenth-century woven coverlets. Each is woven in 100% cotton. The Tyler Lion lap blanket is derived from a coverlet made by Henry Tyler, a prominent nineteenth-century weaver, and uses his lion trademark in the corner blocks. The Peacock lap blanket is interpreted from a wool and cotton coverlet featuring a popular peacock design and was made by James Pearson about 1835. The Ohio Grapevine lap blanket is based on an intricately patterned nineteenth century coverlet made by John Klinhinz. The Geometric Check Lap Blanket is interpreted from a meticulously woven coverlet. Matching and contrasting jacquard pillows also are based on interpretations of these antique coverlets.

Lap Blankets - 54" x 72":	Navy	Delft	Cranberry	Forest	Rose
Tyler Lion	x	x	x		
Geometric Check	x		x	x	
Ohio Grapevine	x	x	x		x
Peacock	x	x	x		x

Pillows: 14" x 14":	Navy	Delft	Cranberry	Forest	Rose
Tyler Lion	x	x	x	x	
Geometric Check	x	x	x	x	
Ohio Grapevine	x	x	x	x	x
Peacock	x	x	x		x

BUTTERMILK PAINTS

After 1800, paints made from various milk derivatives were used widely in America as a substitute for commercial formulations that usually were available only in large urban areas. They are suitable for re-creating traditional techniques such as feathering, combing, stenciling, and many brushing effects. These colors are reproduced from protected areas of paint found on objects in the Abby Aldrich Rockefeller Folk Art Center collection.

BUTTERMILK PAINTS

PAINTED LOOKING GLASS

14-28 Ohio Cupboard Rust Color

7-13 Picture Frame Cream Color

14-29 Ohio Cupboard Blue

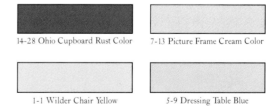
1-1 Wilder Chair Yellow

5-9 Dressing Table Blue

3-6 Fancy Chair Yellow

14-30 Ohio Cupboard Reddish Brown

13-25 Corner Cupboard Yellowish White

2-2 Child's Rocker Bright Red

10-18 Virginia Clock Blue

2-3 Child's Rocker Dark Red (Also available in oil glaze)

3-5 Fancy Chair Green

4-8 Windsor Chair Pink

5-10 Dressing Table Navy Blue (Also available in oil glaze)

CHRISTMAS
IN WILLIAMSBURG TODAY

The wintry night air is filled with the pungent smell of wood smoke and the stirring sounds of fife and drum. A cannon booms, and at the signal, every window in this historic town is lighted with the soft glow of candlelight. Tall, flaming cressets and blazing bonfires light carolers' faces. The Grand Illumination ushers in the holiday season in Williamsburg. For nearly a month, the town, with all its Yuletide festivities, is filled with the anticipation, merriment, and excitement of this special season.

Now Christmas comes, 'tis fit that we
Should feast and sing, and merry be
Keep open house, let fiddlers play
A fig for cold, sing care away . . .

Virginia Almanac, 1766

COLONIAL WILLIAMSBURG DECORATES FOR CHRISTMAS

Decorate your home in style using a book of illustrated step-by-step instructions. *Colonial Williamsburg Decorates for Christmas* can help you make wreaths and plaques, swags and roping, special table arrangements, and other charming accents. Each idea employs natural materials including fresh fruits, fresh greens, and dried herbs and flowers.
1271 Hardbound
1933 Softbound

APPLE CONE

Create traditional yet original table decorations using fresh fruits and greenery. Evenly spaced nails provide a sturdy base. Detailed instructions for suggested designs are included. Height 10".

WASSAIL MIX PACKET

Celebrate the spirit of the season with a Wassail Bowl of hot spiced punch. In England, the bowl was filled with hot ale, toasted apples, sugar, and spices. In eighteenth-century Williamsburg, such hot punches were served from Christmas Eve until Twelfth Night. This special Wassail Mix contains a blend of citrus peel and spices to heat with cider, sherry, or brandy for a modern interpretation of this festive treat.

Left to right: *COLONIAL WILLIAMSBURG DECORATES FOR CHRISTMAS*, APPLE CONE, and WASSAIL MIX PACKET

TREE ORNAMENTS

In 1842, Dr. Charles Minnigerode recalled his childhood in Germany and set up in his parlor Williamsburg's first Christmas tree "dressed with gay colors and candles." These silverplated ornaments are interpretations of eighteenth-century designs of various origins. The Treetop Star Ornament is based on a harness ornament found at the James Geddy House. The Rocking Horse Ornament is interpreted from an engraving dated 1756, while the Toy Drum Ornament is interpreted from snare drums shown in drawings and prints of the period. The Lamb Pull Toy Ornament is taken from an illustration in d'Allemagne's *Histoire des Jouets*. The Doll Ornament is inspired by a doll owned by a member of the prominent Virginia family of President John Tyler.

Handsome brass interpretations of eighteenth-century items also make striking tree ornaments. The Rococo Scroll Ornament is interpreted from a decorative motif on a bracket clock made in London around 1740 by John Elliott. The William and Mary Ornament uses the interwoven royal monogram of these two English monarchs. The Queen Anne Ornament bears the royal monogram of Anne of England, an interwoven "AR" for "Anna Regina."

J17 Treetop Star Ornament
J50 Rocking Horse Ornament
J51 Toy Drum Ornament
J52 Lamb Pull Toy Ornament
J53 Doll Ornament
CW25-12 Rococo Scroll Ornament
CW25-5 William and Mary Ornament
CW25-6 Queen Anne Ornament

J53, CW25-12

Shown clockwise from top: J17, J51, CW25-6, J52, CW25-6, J51, J50, CW25-5, J52

Christmas was a season of reverence, mirth, and fellowship in eighteenth-century Williamsburg. Virginia colonists may have brought with them the English custom of decking homes and churches with greenery. The custom of tree-trimming originated in Williamsburg in 1842 when a professor at the College of William and Mary shared his native German traditions with some children by decorating a small tree "with gay colors and candles."

Today, Williamsburg has become well known for its celebration of Christmas. A huge evergreen is lighted just across the square from the original house where the town's first tree was aglow with candles more than two centuries ago.

Throughout the Historic Area, decorations are created from greenery, and such natural materials as fruits, berries, cones, and nuts. These colorful, handmade decorations are displayed on doorways and windows and delight visitors as they pass each different house.

Musical events occur almost daily as candlelight concerts, madrigal singers, and minstrels entertain. Visitors are invited to join in eighteenth-century dancing and the merriment of "gambols" and lawn games. Feasts abound as special foods and beverages are baked and brewed. The sights, sounds, smells, and especially the spirit of this joyous holiday season are alive in Williamsburg.

DIRECTIONS FOR ORDERING

HOW TO ORDER BY PHONE

Ordering by telephone is the easiest way to place an order. For orders being charged to VISA, MasterCard, or American Express, call TOLL FREE, Monday through Saturday, 9:00 a.m. to 5:00 p.m. Eastern Time: 1-800-446-9240. (Customers in Virginia, Alaska, and Hawaii can call 804-220-7463.) After business hours and on Sundays, an answering service is available to take your order.

For your convenience the Colonial Williamsburg price list includes all costs for shipping within the continental United States, including packing, handling, and insurance. We generally ship by UPS; if you prefer Parcel Post, please let us know. Certain oversize items are shipped via Motor Freight and may require pick up.

Allow two to four weeks for delivery, or longer if engraving or special order items are requested. On occasions when a rush delivery is needed, express service is available for most merchandise. Our sales representatives will explain the procedure and cost when you call our toll-free number.

If you have questions about your order, our Customer Service Department is available Monday through Saturday, 9:00 a.m. to 5:00 p.m. Eastern Time: 804-220-7378. Sorry, we do not accept collect calls.

We proudly and unconditionally guarantee your satisfaction with our merchandise and our service.

WILLIAMSBURG SHOPS

Three decades ago, Colonial Williamsburg began a program to select high quality retail stores throughout the country to carry our distinctive product line. Today there are nearly one hundred official *Williamsburg* Shops. We invite you to visit one to see our fine furnishings and gifts and purchase them locally if you prefer. Call 1-800-446-9240 for the location nearest you.

VISITING COLONIAL WILLIAMSBURG

We look forward to your next visit to Williamsburg and hope you will experience how different shopping can be here. The two Craft Houses will acquaint you with the vast array of products pictured in this catalog. Afterward, visit the Sign of the Rooster for folk art items based on the collections of the Abby Aldrich Rockefeller Folk Art Center. Then stroll down the Duke of Gloucester Street and step into the eighteenth-century world with its bustling general stores and specialty shops.

At the Visitor Center you will find a bookstore and a gift shop for children. Should you desire to purchase a ticket for visiting our exhibition buildings, the Visitor Center should be on your itinerary.

Carter's Grove, the eighteenth-century plantation, is just eight miles from the Historic Area. This beautiful house and museum has archaeological exhibits, a reconstructed slave quarter, and a gift shop.

Every hotel operated by Colonial Williamsburg has its own special shop as do the Golden Horseshoe and Tazewell Clubs. The gift shop at the DeWitt Wallace Decorative Arts Gallery has merchandise based on the museum's vast collection. Shopping at Colonial Williamsburg is varied, interesting, and enjoyable!

The income generated by our visitors' purchases and admissions allows the Colonial Williamsburg Foundation to continue its research and educational programs. This income supports the continued maintenance of the Foundation's exhibition buildings and antique collections, furthers academic research, archaeological excavations, and educational programs, and assists in the acquisition of antiques, rare books, and prints that come to the attention of the curators. The restoration, preservation, and continued research into the eighteenth century and America's colonial heritage depend on this support.

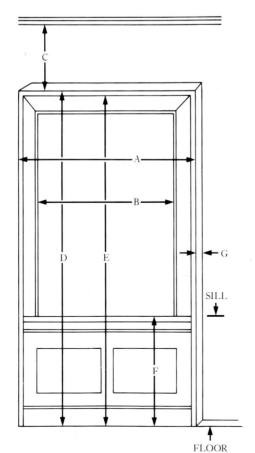

A. Extreme Width
B. Inside Width
C. Top of Trim to Ceiling
D. Extreme Height
E. Inside Height
F. Sill to Floor
G. Return

ADVISORY SERVICES

ADVISORY SERVICES

Colonial Williamsburg has developed an extensive program of customer assistance that we call our Advisory Services. The following services have been developed to fill our customers' needs more fully. As always, satisfaction is guaranteed.

INTERIOR DESIGN ASSISTANCE

Whether you are adding the final touches to an eclectic decor or just beginning with a traditional plan in mind, Colonial Williamsburg will help you coordinate all the details and achieve the look you want. We can help you coordinate our collection of fine fabrics, wallpapers, paints, furniture, and decorative accessories to blend perfectly with the scheme of your home or office. Our custom workshop can custom design and produce window treatments, bed hangings, slipcovers, and other fabric creations. Your needs may be as simple as a wallpaper book, paint chart, or fabric samples — or as complex as a proposal for decorating your entire home. Whatever your needs, we are here to assist you. For more information, call 1-800-446-9240. When you are in Williamsburg, meet the staff of the Craft House Interior Design Studio, or you may reach them by calling 804-220-7503.

BRIDAL REGISTRY

Congratulations on your engagement! The Colonial Williamsburg Bridal Registry is available to brides throughout the United States. When you register, you will receive a copy of the *Williamsburg* Reproductions catalog to help you choose from a wide line of heirloom quality home furnishings and accessories. We will also include our registry packet, which features a checklist for recording gift selections and printed cards with our toll-free number. Family and friends can call and speak with the Bridal Registry Consultant, and order their gift, wrapped and delivered to your door. This service is also available to couples who are celebrating special wedding anniversaries. For more information, please call 1-800-446-9240. In Virginia, Alaska, and Hawaii call 804-220-7463.

ENGRAVING

Personalizing treasured metalwork was a popular practice in colonial days. Our eighteenth-century predecessors engraved their gold and silver jewelry with names, dates, proverbs, or other meaningful phrases, and were partial to engraving monograms and initials on their sterling, brass, and pewter belongings.

The art of freehand engraving is all but lost today. The Colonial Williamsburg crafts program, begun in 1936 to demonstrate and preserve the crafts of the eighteenth century, has kept the art of freehand engraving alive for present and future generations. Our staff of skilled engravers complete a rigorous apprenticeship during which, supervised by two Master Engravers, they learn the various techniques, styles, and practices of freehand and machine-assisted engraving. Both types of engraving are available.

Most jewelry and metal items can be personalized in a variety of lettering styles and applications. Consider the eighteenth-century custom of engraving the bride and groom's first initials over their last for a unique monogram. Please remember to allow additional time for engraving. Sorry, personalized items cannot be returned. For more information, call 1-800-446-9240.

GIFT ASSISTANCE AND WRAPPING

Selecting a distinctive, appropriate gift for that special occasion is effortless with the assistance of our Mail Order staff. One simple phone call replaces all the searching through stores, then wrapping, boxing, and mailing the gift. Let us wrap your gift and have it delivered directly to your special person's door. Our distinctive moiré gift wrap, designed exclusively for Colonial Williamsburg, is available only through mail order. Gift cards are handwritten with your own message. Since there is a charge for this service, and not every item can be gift wrapped, please inquire.

GIFT CERTIFICATES

If you would prefer that the bride, graduate, or special friend make his or her own gift selection, consider a gift certificate from Colonial Williamsburg. We will send a copy of our seasonal mail order brochure along with a handsome gift certificate. We will need your and the recipient's names, complete addresses, and the amount of the gift — $10, $25, $50, $100, or any multiple thereof. For certificates of $350 or more we will include a complimentary copy of the *Williamsburg* Reproductions catalog. Gift certificates are redeemable through mail order or at any of our stores in Williamsburg.

CORPORATE PURCHASES

For information on corporate purchases, please call us at 804-220-7178 or 804-220-7179.

INDEX

All objects illustrated on pages 8-30 are antiques in the collection of the Colonial Williamsburg Foundation. They may be seen in the exhibition buildings in the Historic Area and in the DeWitt Wallace Decorative Arts Gallery.

CREDITS:

DESIGN:
Anita Soos Design

PHOTOGRAPHY:
Sean Kernan Studios
Bill Stites
Jim Fiora
Langdon Clay
Colonial Williamsburg Foundation

COPY:
Ellie MacDougall
Colonial Williamsburg Staff

PRINTING:
Quad/Graphics

LICENSED MANUFACTURERS

THE ADDED TOUCH
1678 Brandon Ave.
Petersburg, VA 23805

1983   Beverage Mixes
        Seeds
        Pomander Balls

BATES FABRICS INC.
P.O. Box 591
Lewiston, ME 04240

1972   Bedspreads

COHASSET COLONIALS
Cohasset, MA 02025

1988   Kit Furniture

**COOPERMAN FIFE
& DRUM CO.**
P.O. Box 242
Centerbrook, CT 06409

1983   Musical Instruments
        Toys

CRUMMLES & CO., USA
726 15th St.
San Francisco, CA 94103

1983   Enameled Boxes

THE DECOY SHOP
Main Street
Bowdoinham, ME 04008

1988   Decoys

THE DIETZ PRESS, INC.
109 E. Cary Street
Richmond, VA 23219

1944   Prints

ELDRED WHEELER
60 Sharp Street
Hingham, MA 02043

1984   Furniture

FOCAL POINT, INC.
P.O. Box 93327
Atlanta, GA 30377-0327

1983   Moldings and
        Chair Rails

**FOREIGN ADVISORY
SERVICE CORP.**
P.O. Box 549
Princess Anne, MD 21853

1958   Crystal
        Delft

**FRIEDMAN BROS.
DECORATIVE ARTS INC.**
9015 NW 105 Way
Medley, FL 33178

1938   Mirrors

THE C. R. GIBSON CO.
32 Knight St.
Norwalk, CT 06856

1987   Paper Products
        Stationery

GMG PUBLISHING
25 W. 43 Street
New York, NY 10036

1983   Address Book
        Notecards

GOODWIN WEAVERS
P.O. Box 314
Blowing Rock, NC 28605

1988   Cotton Throws
        and Pillows

HEDGEROW HOUSE, INC.
230 Fifth Avenue
New York, NY 10001

1983   Prints

**HIGHLAND HOUSE
PUBLISHERS**
500 North Henry Street
Alexandria, VA 22314

1983   Prints

**THE HOMER LAUGHLIN
CHINA CO.**
Sixth & Harrison Streets
Newell, WV 26050

1988   Tavern China

**JOHNSON CREATIVE
ARTS INC.**
445 Main Street
West Townsend, MA 01474

1978   Needlework

KARASTAN
P.O. Box 27050
Greensboro, NC 27425-7050

1981   Rugs

KEDRON DESIGN
P.O. Box 126
Sherborn, MA 01770

1983   Notecards, Prints
        Posters

**THE KIRK STIEFF
COMPANY**
800 Wyman Park Drive
Baltimore, MD 21211

1940   Silver, Pewter

KITTINGER COMPANY
1893 Elmwood Avenue
Buffalo, NY 14207

1936   Furniture

J.J. KORMANN & SON, INC.
P.O. Box 5232
Roanoke, VA 24012

1982   Picture Framing

**LACKAWANNA LEATHER
COMPANY**
P.O. Box 939
Conover, NC 28613

1965   Leather

THE MARTIN SENOUR CO.
15 Midland Building
101 Prospect Ave.
Cleveland, OH 44113

1965   Paints

MORGAN PRODUCTS, LTD.
P.O. Box 2466
Oshkosh, WI 54903

1987   Doors and Mantels

MOTTAHEDEH & CO., INC.
225 5th Avenue
New York, NY 10010

1985   Decorative Porcelain

THE NEW BOSTONIAN
231 Washington Street
Weymouth, MA 02188

1987   Dried Flowers

NEW YORK COPPER CO.
P.O. Box 310-726
Brooklyn, NY 11231

1989   Copper Cookware

**NEW YORK GRAPHIC
SOCIETY, LTD.**
35 River Road
Cos Cob, CT 06807

1983   Prints
        Posters

OVERLY PUBLISHING, INC.
60 Union Ave.
Sudbury, MA 01776

1947   Notecards

PALAIS ROYAL, INC.
923 D. Preston Ave.
Charlottesville, VA 22901

1983   Woven Linens

PIMPERNEL, INC.
3 Warrenton Industrial Park
Warrenton, VA 22186

1979   Placemats

PLAID ENTERPRISES, INC.
P.O. Drawer E
Norcross, GA 30091

1979   Miniature Wallpaper

ROWE POTTERY WORKS, INC.
P.O. Drawer L
Cambridge, WI 53523

1985   Pottery

F. SCHUMACHER & CO.
79 Madison Ave.
New York, NY 10016

1941   Fabrics and Wallpaper

**STEVENS LINEN
ASSOCIATES, INC.**
P.O. Box 220
Webster, MA 01570

1984   Printed Textile Products

STULB'S OLD VILLAGE PAINT
P.O. Box 597
Allentown, PA, 18105

1988   Decorative Paints

UNIVERSE BOOKS
381 Park Ave. South
New York, NY 10016

1985   Calendars
        Gift Books

**VIRGINIA
METALCRAFTERS, INC.**
1010 East Main Street
Waynesboro, VA 22980

1949   Brass and Iron
        Lighting Fixtures
        Locks
        Wooden Accessories

WATERFORD/WEDGWOOD INC.
P.O. Box 1454
Wall, NJ 07719

1930   Dinnerware

**WILLIAMSBURG POTTERY
FACTORY**
Rt. 3, Box 148
Lightfoot, VA 23090

1952   Pottery

THOS. K. WOODARD
835 Madison Avenue
New York, NY 10021

1983   Rugs

**WOODEN PRODUCTS OF
VIRGINIA, INC.**
P.O. Box 13084
Richmond, VA 23225

1982   Toys